A Candlelight Ecstasy Romance®

"A—A MAN OF YOUR . . . STATURE WOULDN'T MAKE LOVE IN AN ELEVATOR. . . . IT ISN'T RESPECTABLE!" TINA GASPED.

"When I'm with you I don't feel respectable," Steve murmured, his mouth buried in her neck. "Besides, I've never made love in an elevator before."

"And you're not going to now, you sex fiend!"

"A sex fiend, am I?" He blocked any attempt of Tina's to escape by placing his hands on either side of her head.

"Steve, please."

"That's what I'm going to do," he responded, his voice full of suppressed passion. "I'm going to please you like you've never been pleased before, honey."

CANDLELIGHT ECSTASY CLASSIC ROMANCES

WINTER'S FLAME

Noelle Berry McCue

A CANDLELIGHT ECSTASY ROMANCE®

Published by
Dell Publishing Co., Inc.
1 Dag Hammarskjold Plaza
New York, New York 10017

ISBN: 0-440-19618-3

Printed in the United States of America

August 1987

10 9 8 7 6 5 4 3 2 1

WFH

To Rosalie Taylor, my sister-in-law and my friend, one who is always willing to listen and ready if I need a shoulder to lean on.

For you, Rosie, because you are special and because I love you.

To Our Readers:

We have been delighted with your enthusiastic response to Candlelight Ecstasy Romances®, and we thank you for the interest you have shown in this exciting series.

In the upcoming months we will continue to present the distinctive sensuous love stories you have come to expect only from Ecstasy. We look forward to bringing you many more books from your favorite authors and also the very finest work from new authors of contemporary romantic fiction.

As always, we are striving to present the unique, absorbing love stories that you enjoy most—books that are more than ordinary romance. Your suggestions and comments are always welcome. Please write to us at the address below.

Sincerely,

The Editors
Candlelight Romances
1 Dag Hammarskjold Plaza
New York, New York 10017

WINTER'S
FLAME

CHAPTER ONE

Christina Taggert felt unusually spiritless when she stepped through the front entrance of Deli-Cacy, the small restaurant and deli that she owned. Glancing across the room, she saw a familiar figure carefully arranging place settings in preparation for the breakfast rush. He moved down the long counter with quick efficiency, his head bent as he concentrated on his task.

Silas Porter had joined her staff after her husband Dennis had been killed in an auto accident, and he'd quickly become indispensable to her. He was willing to work at any task that needed doing, and without his skills as a handyman she was certain this old building would soon cave in on them. Just then he looked up, and the dull throbbing in her temples eased slightly at the first sight of his beaming grin.

"You're supposed to be off this morning," she scolded affectionately. "I swear you're determined to work yourself to death, Si."

His barrel chest expanded with assumed indignation. "I'll have you know I'm as strong as an ox, woman!"

"And twice as hardheaded."

Silas ignored this slight to his character. "Anyway," he remarked, looking oddly embarrassed, "I had a reason for coming in early today."

Tina's brows arched in inquiry, and Silas quickly blurted, "I know I was supposed to help you cater that dinner tonight, but I need to take the time off. Today's our wedding anniversary, and if Della finds out I forgot it again the fat will really be in the fire."

She couldn't resist the urge to tease him. "That ring through your nose is shining rather brightly, Silas dear."

He hitched up his jeans, and the enormous belly that poured over the gold-nugget-studded buckle of his belt shook with mirth. "That woman of mine is a holy terror, all right."

"That woman of yours is four foot eleven, and as gentle as a lamb," Tina corrected. "You should be ashamed of yourself for being such a coward, Si Porter."

"Humph! That little lamb has a way of getting back at a body."

"Does she tie you up and beat you?" she asked with widening eyes. "How kinky!"

"She cries," he corrected aggrievedly.

Tina crossed the wooden floor of the restaurant while Silas shuffled along behind. Entering the kitchen, she removed her heavy parka, and shoved both her jacket and purse into the cupboard Si had converted into a closet. Then she turned with a broad smile to the man still grousing behind her. "A big fella like you afraid of a few measly tears? What ever happened to that macho rodeo rider Della told me she first fell in love with?"

Si gave a rumbling sigh in response. "He went the way of any other stupid dogie, all hog-tied and trussed up as neat as you please."

Tina wouldn't have dreamed of hurting Si's feelings by laughing out loud, although the urge to do so was strong. In the three years she'd known him she had discovered his heart to be as big as his body, but his male ego was fragile. He would never openly admit that he was all bluff and bluster, and she would never think of bringing it to his attention.

She remembered the day she'd glanced up expecting to greet a customer, and instead been approached for a job by this aging, craggy-faced man who had been nervously twisting a battered Stetson between his blunt-tipped fingers.

"I'm sorry about your husband, Mrs. Taggert," he had said, his condolence all the more poignant for being so quietly uttered. "My name is Silas Porter. Kathy Sue and my wife are real good friends, and she suggested I stop by. She's been worrying about you managing this place with all you got to deal with. I can turn my hand to most things, and I'd sure appreciate the chance to help out some."

Kathy Sue Durham was the waitress she and Dennis had hired when they first opened, a buxom, bleached-blond dynamo who drew customers to the deli like bees to a honeycomb. Her breezy, good-natured manner hid a sensitivity that Tina had come to depend on since her husband's unexpected death. At this further sign of the older woman's concern she had fought to suppress tears, which in those nightmare days had usually hovered too close to the surface.

"I . . . ." She'd cleared her throat, and begun again. "I couldn't pay you much more than minimum wage right now, Mr. Porter."

His voice had been loudly convivial, but the eyes that met hers had held quiet understanding as he said, "You'd be doing me a favor, Mrs. Taggert. This here retirement business don't sit well on my shoulders, and my wife's getting mighty tired of having me underfoot all day."

She had held out her hand, and felt it swallowed up in a warm, comforting clasp. "My name's Tina."

"I'm proud to know you," he'd said shyly. "Please, call me Si."

Tina thought of those words now, and realized she was the one who was proud to know this kind, gentle giant. There was no hair on the top of his head, and the coarse whitened wisps that stubbornly remained stuck out over his large ears. He looked like an aging Kewpie doll, and a rush of emotion tightened her throat as she placed a hand on his brawny arm.

"You know you don't have to give me any explanations when you want some time off," she said quietly. "You've been my friend and my source of sanity too long for that, Si."

A painfully vivid flush darkened his already ruddy cheekbones, and he gave her a sheepish grin. "Kind of figured you'd feel that way. I was almost asleep when I remembered this here anniversary, so I snuck out of bed and called Kathy Sue. She's agreed to fill in for me at that shindig tonight, so she won't be in till this afternoon. I'll play waiter for breakfast."

A slight frown altered the perfect arch of Tina's brows. Without thinking she blurted, "I wish we hadn't agreed to cater this party."

He seemed surprised by her admission, and she couldn't blame him. She wasn't usually so negative, and she knew the apprehension she felt about tonight's affair must have him puzzled. Since she herself didn't understand why she felt so uneasy, she could hardly clarify her emotions for Si.

In an obvious attempt at reassurance he remarked, "This dinner's no different than a hundred others we've catered, honey."

"It's our client I'm worried about."

"What about him?"

Tina averted her eyes, feeling suddenly flustered. "Steven Michaels is a prominent figure around here, Si."

15

"That's all to the good, isn't it?" He tugged at the lobe of his ear, his confusion evident as he looked at her. "Gaining Michaels as a customer is quite a feather in our cap, Tina."

She shifted her feet nervously. "But if he's not satisfied with our services we could lose a lot of our regular clientele. You know as well as I do that quite a few people in this town would be swayed by his opinion."

Silas shook an admonishing finger in her face. "Now, don't you be letting false modesty get in the way of good business. You've done a heck of a job catering parties, and I've heard many a compliment on your cooking."

She grimaced wryly. "There's always a first time, and in Mr. Michaels's case it could well be our last."

"He struck me as a fair man, and as long as we give him what he's asked for, everything will be fine."

"Well," she argued with uncharacteristic belligerence, "from what I've heard about him he strikes me as the kind of person who wouldn't care if his demands were unreasonable."

Si's drawled reply was succinct and to the point. "He expects the best and is used to getting it. What's so unusual about that?"

Tina's shoulders slumped as she realized the futility of their argument. She tried to think of a way logically to explain her uneasiness to Si, and yet she was as bewildered by her attitude as he was.

She remembered amber eyes that should have been warm, but they had held a depth of cool calculation that had chilled her. They had been the eyes of a predator.

She shivered, amazed at her ability to recall the details of his appearance with such clarity. His hair had a healthy sheen, a rich tobacco-brown that had made her wonder what its thickness would feel like between her fingers. He was tall, well over six feet, and his broad shoulders and lean hips had been emphasized by the snug fit of his jeans. Her mouth had gone curiously dry when she noted the dark tufts of hair exposed by the opening of his blue linen shirt.

Those piercing golden-brown eyes had left her feeling vulnerable. Yet it wasn't the physical appeal of his face and body that had made her nervous, she realized. She'd met other handsome men without coming apart at the seams, but there had been something disturbingly different about Steven Michaels. It had been his overt masculinity—the aura of power and ruthlessness she sensed in him that made her catch her breath.

He had looked at her as though he were considering buying her at auction like one of the precious quarterhorses he raised, and she had resented it so much she had been tempted to open her mouth and show him her teeth. Instead she had taken the cowardly way out and escaped through the door leading to the kitchen as fast as her long legs would carry her.

A nerve pulsed beside her mouth as she recalled her craven behavior, which did nothing to lessen the resentment she felt toward the cause of all this soul searching. She muttered absentmindedly, "I knew he'd be difficult to please the moment I saw him."

Silas had been inspecting the toe of his boot, which he kept shined to a high gloss. At Tina's admission his head jerked up. "I didn't know you'd met him before."

She traced a finger over the cold metal grill and shrugged with feigned nonchalance. "We haven't met . . . I mean I've never actually spoken to him. I was here the day he came in, remember?"

A brief silence ensued while Si searched his memory. Then he looked up, a wicked glint in his eyes. "Handsome devil, isn't he?"

She pursed her mouth primly. "I didn't notice."

"Now that I recollect, for someone who didn't notice the man you sure backed off like a nervous filly."

"I was in a hurry," she remarked defensively. "Kathy Sue and I were late for a children's party we were catering that afternoon."

"Well, he sure noticed you." Si's features reflected sudden comprehension, and his mocking snort was loud in the room. "Now I know why he kept looking toward the kitchen. I thought he seemed a mite bothered when we discussed the arrangements for his dinner party. If I had known he'd seen you, I would have guessed why soon enough. You're a fine figure of a woman."

Tina's cheeks grew as hot as a potbellied stove. "Don't be ridiculous!"

Si's innocent look made her grit her teeth in exasperation. "He asked an awful lot of questions, and not many of them were about food."

"What do you mean?"

"Well, he wanted to know how many employees we had, and I pointed to Kathy Sue and myself. Then he asked who owned the restaurant, and when I told him your name he began to question me about you."

She stiffened. "Personal questions?"

He shook his head and patted her arm consolingly. "Now, don't be getting on your high horse. I only gave him your name, rank, and serial number."

Her eyes narrowed suspiciously. "You didn't by any chance mention that I'm a widow?"

This time it was Silas who shifted uneasily. "I might have let it drop during our conversation."

"Oh, Si!"

"I could tell he wasn't impressed with the size of our operation," he said, avoiding the accusation in her eyes by grabbing a rag to wipe down the already clean grill. "I admit I thought he might be more disposed to hire us if he knew what a gutsy little lady you are."

"I am not a 'little' anything," she said heatedly.

"I'm five foot eight, and at the moment I don't feel very ladylike, Silas Porter!"

He winced at her use of his full name, but stuck to his convictions. "Just like I said, you're a fine figure of a woman."

Tina couldn't tell which emotion held the greatest sway over her mind in that instant—frustration, anger, or amusement. Luckily for Si's peace of mind, amusement won out. "You are incorrigible, do you know that? I know you were just thinking of my welfare, but from now on there will be no more 'poor widow-woman' nonsense to drum up business. Agreed?"

Her forgiving attitude gave Silas all the encouragement he needed to return to his usual blustering protectiveness. His repentant expression was replaced with a worried scowl. "Della and I can celebrate our anniversary tomorrow night. If Michaels signed with us because he fancies you, then I don't want you going to his place alone. Now that I bring it to mind, the man has quite a reputation with the ladies."

"I won't be alone," she reminded him with a grin. "Kathy Sue will be with me."

"Another female won't be much protection."

"Don't let her hear you say that."

"Yeah, she'd jump on her feminist high-horse and get Della all fired up." He shook his head in an attitude of genuine bewilderment as he muttered beneath his breath, "Women!"

Tina gave a choked laugh, her eyes gleefully inspecting his disgruntled features. "We get on your nerves, do we?"

"A man tries to show a little concern, and what does he get for his trouble? He gets made fun of, that's what!"

Tina struggled to compose herself, knowing how sensitive Si was on this particular subject. "I appreciate your concern, but what do you think Mr. Michaels is going to do, ravish me in the middle of the festivities?"

When he didn't respond to her attempt at humor, she reached up and kissed his weathered cheek. "Just because the man looked at me doesn't mean you have to flap over me like a mother hen, Si. You and Della go out and enjoy yourselves."

He gave a resigned sigh, but sent her a warning look. "All right, but I'm going to make sure Kathy Sue keeps an eye on you."

She placed clenched fists against her hips and sucked in an exasperated breath. "You and Kathy Sue are going to baby me to death!"

He patted her back self-consciously, his usual good humor restored. "Now, don't you be givin' me none of yore sassy looks," he admonished, his exaggerated drawl loud enough to shatter glass, "or I'll sic Della on you!"

Twilight was shading from purple to black, and towering evergreens cast forbidding shadows against the sky as Tina turned off the county road she'd been following for the last fifteen minutes.

21

Immediately gravel crunched beneath the wheels of the lumbering blue-and-white catering van, and she ground her teeth together as she hit a gaping pothole.

Her mouth quirked with wry humor when she realized she could probably walk faster than she was driving, but visibility was so poor she didn't dare pick up speed. The clouds overhead looked dark rimmed and angry, and were quickly swallowing up the little daylight remaining. A storm was all she needed, she thought, the headache she'd been fighting for hours increasing in intensity.

Tiredly she rolled down the window and drew the cold, moist air into her lungs. It was a good thing Si had already left for home when Kathy Sue sliced her palm open with the meat cleaver, she thought, or he would have canceled his plans for the evening. Spoiling an anniversary celebration would have really added to her depressed mood, although she didn't see how she could feel worse than she already did.

Luckily the last of the lunch crowd had been served, and they were ready to close the restaurant when the accident occurred. She had rushed Kathy Sue to the emergency clinic to have her hand stitched, and then taken her home. During the drive her friend had cussed a blue streak, furious with herself for having been so clumsy.

"You didn't purposely cut your hand to get out

of working tonight," Tina had finally said in exasperation.

"Just give me a minute to change out of these bloodstained clothes," Kathy Sue retorted, "and we'll just see who won't be working tonight!"

"You won't, for one," she said, the firmness of her voice leaving no room for argument. "You are going to take two of those pain tablets the doctor gave you and crawl into bed where you belong."

Kathy Sue's stubborn features were pale, but she wasn't one to give in lightly. "You can't serve a party of that size by yourself, and I don't like the sound of this guy Michaels."

"It will be easy—I'll arrange a buffet table. By the way, since when do you listen to anything Si says? You know he thinks women are weak and need looking after."

Tina's reference to Si's chauvinistic tendencies was a stroke of genius.

"Della should have straightened him out a long time ago, but she prefers to let him think he's boss," Kathy Sue said with a shake of her head.

Tina was quick to use her advantage. "You know that I'm perfectly capable of looking out for myself."

"Not where men like Steven Michaels are concerned!"

There was an unmistakable trembling in her friend's voice, and Tina decided not to argue. Giving her a worried glance, she remarked, "You look

23

like hell, Kathy Sue. Now, lay your head back against that seat and stop your grumbling."

But the older woman was on a roll, and by the time Tina got her tucked into bed she was tempted to gag her. She remembered how many times Si had voiced the same wish, and now she could fully sympathize with him. Kathy Sue's intentions were good, but she could be wearing on the nerves.

Tina listened to the odd sounds coming from the engine and anxiously nibbled the full, pouting curve of her lower lip. Her mechanical expertise was embarrassingly negligible, and she hadn't the slightest idea what was causing that irritating pinging beneath the hood. She could check the oil, change a tire, and fill the radiator with water, but she drew a blank when it came to remedying odd noises.

Poor old Gertie wasn't long for this world if she didn't get some professional attention. Since Dennis's death she'd let all but the most crucial repairs slide. By the time the bills were paid at the end of each month there just never seemed to be enough money left to repair the van.

The cumbersome vehicle shuddered over another hole, and her head bumped painfully against the roof. "Gertie's shocks are nothing to write home about either," she muttered.

Tina's foot pressed against the accelerator as the narrow road became a steep gradient. Her hands tightened as she felt the engine cough ominously, and she glanced nervously around her. Dark evergreens towered over the road on both sides, and the only sign of civilization was an occasional telephone pole. Not the best place to break down, she thought ruefully.

The deeper Tina drove into the woods, the more uneasy she became. The realization that she was a city girl at heart made her grin with deprecating honesty. Both she and Dennis had been born and raised in the Bay Area. Yet when they began to search for a place to fulfill their dream of opening their own restaurant, they chose this small town located in the foothill country of California's Sierra Nevada mountains. Although they loved San Francisco, they had wanted more than concrete playgrounds for the children they'd planned to have.

Tina flinched at the memory and tried to think of something else. She felt isolation enclose her like an impenetrable shroud. When the first heavy drops of rain began to slide down the windshield of the van they looked too much like tears, reminding her of how she had once given in to the apathy of despair. She caught her breath sharply as she remembered being pressed to a body vibrant with life, and a sheen of moisture filmed her eyes.

She conquered her urge to cry, but it wasn't as easy to restrain her thoughts. She missed having someone with whom to share her life and her dreams, she realized sadly; and she sometimes ached to be held. Death was such a final, indefensible barrier. Although she had learned to control her weaknesses and utilize her strengths, she felt locked in an emotional prison. She wanted to love and to be loved again; to need and be needed.

Suddenly the memory of a pair of devilish golden eyes rose in her mind, and she berated herself for the foolishness of her imagination. Steven Michaels was safe to fantasize about, she thought, but he would be a dangerous man to love. She was not the kind of woman to be content with an affair, and from what she'd heard about him he would never think of offering anything else. She tried to convince herself that she was too sensible to let him disturb her hard-won peace of mind, but the closer she got to his ranch the more unsettled she became.

Tina's reveries were abruptly shattered when the van gave a series of jerks. Her apprehension increased in direct proportion to the steam hissing from Gertie's hood. By now the pinging had become an urgent thudding, and as she rounded a bend in the road she was relieved to see a glimmer of light filtering through the trees. She urged on the halting vehicle. "Just a little farther, old girl."

With a determination painfully learned in the months following her husband's death, Tina reached deep within herself for the core of strength that had sustained her during those dark days. Some people might call that inner strength hope, she thought, while some might say it was faith. For her it was necessity, and the word had a very lonely sound.

CHAPTER TWO

Steven Michaels glanced down at his watch and scowled. His guests would be arriving in less than two hours, and the people from the catering service hadn't shown up yet. Restless, he paced the wooden veranda that ran the length of his cedar ranch house. He angrily searched the gathering darkness, listening for the sound of an approaching vehicle with barely contained impatience.

Engaging the services of Deli-Cacy Catering had been a logical choice, since they were located relatively close to his home. Yet logic hadn't played a key part in his decision, he admitted with rueful honesty. He mentally kicked himself for behaving like a boy with an overactive sex drive. Although Deli-Cacy had come well recommended, he should have known better than to trust a business run by a woman, he thought.

A derisive curve molded his mouth as he realized what he would be called by most of the women he knew if he voiced such a sentiment; but they could throw any names they wanted at him.

In forty years of living he had never come across a trustworthy female, and at this late date he doubted if he ever would.

Ironically, at that moment an image seduced his mind, the woman who had inspired him to so impulsively hire the Deli-Cacy people to cater his party. Although he was disgusted with himself for letting his judgment be swayed by a pretty face, something about that female haunted him. He had been drawn to her in a mysterious manner he still couldn't comprehend, let alone accept. At the time all he'd known for certain was that he had to see her again.

Steve gripped the wooden post at his side as he visualized wavy hair the color of warm caramel, and a sensuously full-lipped mouth curved with the laughter he had been too far away to share. The glimpse he had caught of her had been fleeting, but it had been enough to capture his interest in a way he found disturbing. He had been attracted to many women over the years, but never with the suddenness or force he'd experienced that afternoon. No, he thought, as he felt a rush of desire tighten his body. There had been little logic involved in his choice of caterers.

He had come to town to restock his household provisions and buy grain for his horses, and had impulsively dropped into the restaurant recommended by a friend. As much as he hated entertaining, for quite some time he had been thinking about repaying all of his social obligations with one large dinner party. When he'd realized that he was less than a half block from Deli-Cacy's front door, he'd decided to check out the possibility of acquiring their services.

The name of the place had almost put him off, and his features had expressed his disdain as he viewed the lacy white curtains tied back from wooden-paned windows. But when he'd looked through the glass from the street and seen the small, round tables covered by gingham cloth and baskets of plants hanging from the ceiling, he'd been surprised to discover that the restaurant had a rustic charm which appealed to him.

Nickel and brass lamps had glowed cosily, illuminating a restaurant that was comfortably homey. It had seemed to promise shelter from the cold October wind that pierced the folds of his heavy, fleece-lined jacket. He had felt like a hungry little boy with his nose pressed to a bakery window, and that sudden realization had put him on the defensive.

He hadn't liked being reminded of his childhood with such painful clarity, recalling too much time spent on the outside looking in at the people who belonged. His mouth had been set in a hard line as he pushed open the thick wooden door and entered the restaurant. His eyes had been hooded with remembered pain when he glanced across the room and saw her.

She'd been standing behind a long counter, speaking over her shoulder to an elderly, heavyset man wearing the typically western attire of worn jeans and a plaid wool shirt. Steve's mind had focused on the sound of her melodious laugh, which rippled over him like a physical caress. Then his attention had been captured by a pair of sparkling eyes, and the breath had left his body in a sudden rush. Although he tried to tell himself he'd simply been too long without the solace of a female body, he couldn't fool himself. From that moment on there had been only one woman he wanted in his bed, and that woman was Christina Taggert.

Remembering the disturbing emotions he'd felt that day, he muttered an obscenity beneath his breath and again began to pace the length of the veranda. He suspected that his present irritability had less to do with the failure of the catering firm to arrive than with disappointment at the possibility of not seeing the woman who dominated his thoughts. Since Silas had told him that the catering service was his employer's particular pride, he'd been fairly certain she would show up tonight. Although he'd spent the last two weeks trying to convince himself otherwise, the memory of shining reddish brown waves and wide, emerald-green eyes was fast becoming an obsession.

A sudden frown deepened the creases beside Steve's mouth as he stared into the distance, alerted by a sound that rose above the rain-laden wind. As he stood there the racket increased, muffled only by a rumbling clap of thunder. For a brief instant the sky was illuminated by lightning, and he spotted a van topping the rise. As it turned into his circular graveled driveway, he shook his head in dismayed recognition.

The disreputable vehicle lurched forward like a drunken sailor, and only when it shuddered to a stop in front of him did he realize he'd been holding his breath. His first sight of the disheveled figure hunched over the steering wheel caused him to give a hearty sigh of relief. At the same moment a hiss of steam escaped from beneath the battered blue hood. A brooding expression darkening his eyes, Steve took the porch steps two at a time.

He ignored the pounding rain that swiftly saturated his hair, running in a torrent down the open collar of his shirt. His eagerness to wrench open the van's door made his heart thud in his chest, and he strove to compose his features. Unbeknownst to him, his effort to appear cool and calm lent a forbidding cast to his features. When he bent down to peer into the vehicle, a pair of apprehensive eyes gazed up at him.

She rolled down the window. "Sorry I'm late, Mr. Michaels."

He stared intently into mysterious depths that increased his pulse beat to a sickening rhythm. Their impact on his senses was so devastating that the reassuring words he'd wanted to say were completely forgotten. All he could think of was the danger she'd been in driving a vehicle that seemed fit only for the scrap heap. And unless Porter was hiding in the back, he thought angrily, she had come alone. His voice was harsh as he glared at her. "What in the hell were you thinking of, coming all the way up here in this bucket of bolts? This thing isn't a catering van, it's a damn death trap!"

The outside world suddenly seemed hazy and indistinct as Steven Michaels loomed over the side of the van. Tina flinched visibly at the angry tone of his voice. His presence was too strong a force for her to deal with, and her reactions too diverse for her to understand. She was bewildered by his obvious resentment toward her, and felt momentarily at a loss for words.

There was a look in his hooded eyes she found disturbing, a brief flickering of emotion that was quickly banked. It was like looking through a mirror and failing to see a reflection. The imagery was all too vivid, and she had the impression that Steven Michaels was skilled at shielding his inner self from possible invasion. All of a sudden she was more afraid than she'd ever been in her life . . . afraid of herself as well as of him.

Tina adopted a similar defensiveness, and her reply was tightly controlled as she replied, "There was nothing in our agreement about my mode of transportation, Mr. Michaels."

"Then there should have been," he retorted impatiently, shaking the wet hair from his forehead as he stared down at her with accusing eyes. "Considering our present circumstances, I think I have the right to question the efficiency of your catering service, Mrs. Taggert. I don't relish the prospect of being embarrassed in front of my guests."

He heard his voice lashing out at her with inexcusable sarcasm, but it was too late to recall his words. The closed look on her face made him cringe in self-disgust, and although he wanted to apologize for his rudeness he was still too angry to act rationally. "Don't you realize you could have been stranded in the middle of nowhere, or struck by lightning, or blinded by rain and run into a damn tree! Don't you have a grain of common sense? Driving around in that thing you are an accident just waiting to happen! For an intelligent woman, you obviously need a keeper," he finished heatedly.

She gasped, her eyes the color of a stormy sea. "It would take a better man than you, Mr. Michaels!"

Still goaded by his temper, he drawled, "I didn't realize I'd applied for the job."

Tina felt as though her entire body were flooded with heat, her humiliation complete. However, she was determined not to show her mortification by so much as the flicker of an eyelash. Unaware of the hurt look in her eyes, she immediately covered with a self-confidence that earned his admiration even as it increased his irritation.

"Where is your kitchen located, Mr. Michaels?"

"It's around the back," he replied, feeling that he'd strangle her if she "Mr. Michaelsed" him one more time. "Why?"

"I need to unload my supplies and move my van out of your driveway," she explained with exaggerated patience, trying to hide her resentment. She knew that she'd failed when she saw the sudden narrowing of his eyes. "I certainly wouldn't want to cause you any embarrassment."

He was already embarrassed, and her quiet dignity did nothing to lessen his shame. His voice was gruffer than he'd intended when he demanded, "Slide over."

She automatically responded to his tone of authority which didn't do much to improve her temper. He had barely settled himself behind the wheel when she muttered, "I know you doubt my capabilities, but I assure you I can drive around your house without hitting it. After all, I managed to get this far, didn't I?"

"By the skin of your teeth."

He turned the key in the ignition, and the terrible noise that resulted made her flinch self-consciously. Poor Gertie managed to lurch a few feet before the engine died. There was a moment of silence, and then Steve remarked in a sardonic voice, "So much for hiding the evidence."

Tina felt as though the top of her head were going to blow off, only this time she couldn't blame the headache she'd been fighting all day. This bossy, conceited cowboy wasn't going to play lord of the manor with her, she vowed, her control deserting her. "You—you arrogant snob! If Gertie isn't attractive enough to share parking space with

34

your illustrious guests, then you can darn well push her out of the way yourself!"

"Gertie?"

She shot him a glance that could have curdled milk, and crossed her arms over her chest. Her bottom lip felt like it was sticking out a mile, but she didn't care what impression she made. Let him think her petulant and childish, she decided, because she was too damn mad to care. How dare he insult her and then smile like that? She wanted to tell him as much, but she'd already made up her mind not to speak to him.

"Do you always sulk when you're angry?"

Her hands clenched into fists at the hint of laughter in his voice. Forgetting her resolution to remain silent, she snapped, "I am not sulking!"

"Then will you look at me if I tell you I'm sorry for upsetting you?"

She shifted uneasily, turning to stare at him in amazement. "You're apologizing?"

His deep chuckle did amazing things to her pulse rate, and she gazed at his smiling mouth in rapt attention when he said, "Even arrogant snobs can be taught manners, and for the record, I don't give a damn who sees . . . ummm, Gertie . . . in my driveway. That's not why I've been acting like a bear with a sore paw."

It wasn't the most original comparison he might have made, but since his example was apt she wasn't going to argue with him. Instead, she decided to respond with a comparison of her own. "I guess I just rub you the wrong way."

His eyes were intent as they looked into her own. "You rub me very much the right way, honey."

She swallowed heavily, at a loss how to handle this unexpected shift in their conversation. Deciding that avoidance was the best policy, she pretended not to notice the sparks flying between them. Clearing her throat, she admitted, "You had every right to be annoyed when I didn't show up on time. I imagine you were worried about your dinner party."

"To hell with the party," he said harshly. "I was afraid you weren't going to show up at all, and I'd been looking forward to seeing you again."

Before she could stop herself, she protested, "But you practically snapped my head off the moment I arrived!"

He leaned his forearm against the steering wheel. "That was because you were stupid enough to come all this way alone. If anything had happened to you, I would have felt responsible."

Her hackles rose at his opinion of her intelligence, not to mention his misguided sense of duty. This discussion was becoming entirely too personal, and it was time she remembered what she was here for. Taking a deep breath, she tilted her chin determinedly. "Deli-Cacy Catering is known for dependability, which is something I pride myself on. While I'm on the subject, your guests will be arriving soon and I really should begin arranging the buffet."

"Considering the weather, I doubt if too many will show up."

His voice held a hopeful note that she chose to ignore. "Either way, I believe in being prepared." She hesitated, her expression wry. "If you don't mind moving, I'll slide out on your side."

He grinned in sudden comprehension. "The passenger door is jammed?"

She felt like a traitor as she nodded. "Unfortunately."

Without another word of criticism Steve opened the door and got out. As he waited for her to slide across the seat he shivered in the icy wind, and wondered if there would be snow on the ground before morning. It was early in the year for it to be this cold, which probably meant they were in for a hard winter.

All thoughts of the weather abruptly left his mind as Tina swung her legs from under the steering column. The serviceable tan raincoat she wore parted, revealing a lacy white blouse tucked into a fitted black skirt. The outfit, which served as a uniform, seemed almost austere, ntil she began to scoot forward on the seat.

Steve's attention was captured by the smooth swish of silken material. Beneath the muted dashboard lights the mental image he'd formed of a reserved woman with Victorian inclinations was quickly revised. Before her hand reached out to close the center kick pleat he glimpsed a black garter belt, and milky-white skin above gossamer-fine nylons. He sucked in a strangled breath and wondered what other feminine delights were hidden by her demure clothing.

The warmth that had begun to grow in the pit of his stomach quickly spread to the juncture of his thighs, and he felt his pants tighten uncomfortably. Stunned by the immediacy of his response, he was unable to move as her feet swung gracefully to the ground.

Steve had to clench his hands at his sides to keep from reaching for her, and appreciated the distraction the pounding rain provided. His shirt was plastered to his chest and back, and his moisture-laden pants chafed the inside of his thighs as he shifted his weight from one leg to the other.

The chill discomfort relaxed his overstimulated body. God, he couldn't believe the effect she was having on him! His nerve endings felt as taut as coiled springs, and just as likely to snap from being overwound. He didn't like the rush of emotion flooding through him, or the growing certainty that this woman, wet and bedraggled as she was, could satisfy the longing he'd always had for something undefinable.

As a child he had learned not to need anyone, and by the time he became a young man he was already self-sufficient. His jaw flexed as he clamped his lips together, concentrating on controlling the violence of his reaction to her. Even though he'd regained some control over his body, when she looked up at him through spiky wet lashes there was nothing he could do to disguise the raw sensuality she provoked.

The expression on his face caused Tina's pulse to quicken in alarm, and she was hardly aware of the words forming in her mind as she nervously licked her lips. "I think we—"

"Do that again."

Her eyes widened in bewilderment. "Do what?"

"Taste the rain on your mouth."

She tensed, careful to keep her tongue where it belonged. "You are being offensive, Mr. Michaels."

"My name is Steve."

Suddenly exasperated, she snapped, "Will you stop staring?"

"But I like looking at you."

It wasn't the cold air that caused her flesh to rise in goose bumps. His low voice matched the heat in his steady gaze, and the simple honesty of his reply unnerved her. "I . . . this is ridiculous."

Tina had never felt more conspicuous in her life. Here she was, standing in a downpour and gaping at a man like an awestruck teenager. She felt off balance, and her nervousness increased as she sensed the power of his tall, muscular body. He was too close, and her lungs felt like they were stuffed with cotton wool.

He reached out and traced the side of her face with a single marauding finger, and her betraying gasp could be heard over the drumming of the

39

rain. His voice was curiously unsteady as he said, "You're a beautiful woman, Christina."

"Right now I'm an angry woman," she argued half heartedly.

"You're confused by what's happening between us, and maybe a little frightened," he corrected gently, "but you're not angry."

He was right, and the knowledge left her nonplused. She was in the middle of nowhere with a man who was coming on to her with all the subtlety of a rocket bursting from a launch pad, and the one emotion she didn't feel was anger. Oddly enough, there was also no fear, and she spoke without questioning her need to reassure him. "I'm not afraid of you."

His hand dropped to his side, but his gaze was steady as he looked at her. "Maybe we should be afraid of each other, Christina."

"You might be right," she whispered shakily, unable to break away from the spell his eyes were casting upon her. She tried to distract herself by concentrating on the fresh smells on the rain-laden wind, but without success. She was too conscious of another, more provocative scent. It was the clean, musky aroma of heated male flesh, and she wondered half-hysterically how he could be hot when it was so damn cold out here.

Steve saw the tremor that shook her body, and cursed himself for being an insensitive idiot. "As you said, keeping you out here in a downpour is ridiculous. Let's get into the house."

Tina's hands trembled as she clumsily re-arranged her raincoat, tightening the belt at her waist. Forgetting Steve's earlier request, she once again flicked out the tip of her tongue to taste the damp residue clinging to her lips. Immediately his expression grew hungry as he avidly followed the movement with his eyes.

Tina immediately realized that she was being seduced by an expert, and that knowledge gave her the strength she needed to break free of his mesmerizing stare. Her movements were jerky and uncoordinated as she stepped to the side of the van, but she was relieved to have something to distract her attention.

As she threw open the sliding side door to begin unloading her supplies, his gruff voice came from behind her, and she jumped nervously when a pair of muscular arms reached past her. "You go on into the house. I'll carry these inside for you."

Tina opened her mouth to protest, but when she turned around and saw his sincere smile, the words fled her mind. Instead she stood aside, feeling self-conscious. She waited while he lifted two heavy boxes with effortless grace, mumbling her thanks as he turned to climb the veranda steps. Striving to regain her composure, she grabbed a smaller box and followed him without being entirely certain that her legs were going to hold her up.

CHAPTER THREE

The stark beauty of the cedar-and-glass A-frame captured Tina's imagination the minute she stepped across the threshold. Dark wooden beams bisected a cathedral ceiling that rose at least forty feet, and a wrought iron staircase curved from the living room to an upper landing. Her eyes followed its path, her delighted appreciation obvious to the man at her side.

"You seem fascinated by my bedroom. I'd be happy to show it to you."

Tina almost dropped the box she was holding. "That's quite all right, I can see enough from here."

Steve was gaining immense pleasure from baiting her, fascinated by the color brightening her cheeks. "But from here you can't see the skylight above my bed. On a clear night the stars seem close enough to touch."

She arched a quizzical brow and gave him as distant a smile as she could manage. "Then there's

42

really no point in my admiring your view, since this evening the sky is far from clear."

He gave a shout of laughter. "You know, I've always gone for body and fluff, Christina. It's quite refreshing to come across a smart lady with a practical streak. Come on," he said abruptly, gesturing with a nod of his head for her to follow him. "Let's get this stuff unloaded, and I'll help you set up the buffet you mentioned. You can check out my skylight when the view can be fully appreciated."

His murmured words were tantalizing, and Tina tried to imagine how he must feel, relaxing in a haven high above the rest of the world. But she doubted if Steven Michaels was content with just star gazing. He would be more likely to prop himself up on pillows, his golden eyes surveying the forested splendor of his land. Like an eagle, she thought fancifully, independent and alone—fiercely protective of his freedom.

Of course, she decided cynically, considering his reputation with women it was doubtful that he spent too many nights alone in his bed. In her line of work it wasn't always possible to avoid gossip, and if some of the things she'd heard were true, he was extremely sensual; as appreciative of attractive women as they were of him.

And he *was* physically appealing . . . damnably so. She could imagine his dusky skinned body sprawled against white silken sheets, eyes issuing a seductive invitation few women would want to resist. The color in her cheeks deepened as she found herself wondering what it would be like to be invited into the eagle's lair.

Shocked at the direction her thoughts were taking, Tina struggled silently to reassure herself. Her curiosity had no chance of being satisfied, since such an invitation wasn't likely to be offered to someone as ordinary as she was. Even if it were, she realized with inward mockery, she was definitely not good mistress material. There were women who could engage in temporary relationships without losing too much of themselves, but she wasn't one of them. This man at her side might be the stuff from which fantasies were made, but she was sensible enough to prefer reality.

Or was she? she thought, watching the sway of his lean hips as she followed him into a large country kitchen. His linen slacks seemed to have shrunk, deliciously emphasizing every line of his hard, compact body. She swallowed a sudden lump in her throat, quickly tearing her gaze away.

She was concentrating so hard on not looking at him that the sound of his voice made her jump. "You stay in here out of the rain while I push the van around back and bring in the rest of your supplies."

He didn't give her a chance to argue but simply deposited the boxes he was carrying on a nearby counter and went back outside. Again her eyes followed him, and she bit her lips as he lowered his head against the pelting rainfall. His body moved with the sinuous grace of superb fitness, his stride long and athletic as he braved the elements. Since he still hadn't bothered to put on a jacket, his soaking-wet shirt clung to the muscles of his back.

Tina's heart pounded frantically as she stared at the muscular contours of his broad shoulders, which rippled provocatively with every movement of his arms. It took an immense effort for her to turn from the doorway, and her hands shook as she hung up her coat in the adjacent laundry room. Extremely irritated with her vacillating emotions, she mentally shook herself as she began to unload the food for his dinner party.

It took several trips to the van before everything was inside, but eventually Steve returned with the last of her provisions. She could feel his stare as she stood at the sink, and braced herself before she turned to thank him for his help.

"What do you think?"

For a moment she stared at him blankly, the words *handsome, sexy, erotic* coming immediately to mind. She nearly blurted them out loud, until she realized he was referring to the kitchen. Grateful to have been given a diversion from her dangerous thoughts, she stared around her in appreciation. "It's lovely."

He set down a stacked set of Tupperware containers on the butcher-block counter in the center of the room, and reached over to snitch a piece of raw cauliflower from the tray of appetizers she'd arranged. He cocked his head in her direction, and there was a teasing inflection in his voice as he said, "I'd expected a little more enthusiasm from a cook of your reputation."

She didn't know what to do with her hands now that they were empty, so she brushed her palms nervously against the folds of her skirt. She found the amusement on his face far too enticing, and she shyly lowered her eyes to the middle button on his shirt. The backward step she took was unobtrusive, but necessary if she wished to continue breathing. "I love the wooden floors, they're so much more appealing than tile or linoleum."

"Keeping them polished is a pain."

"Oh, but the visual effect is worth the extra effort," she remarked earnestly. "The rich grain of the wood in the floor and cabinets ties everything together quite beautifully. With all these modern appliances a kitchen this size might seem rather austere otherwise. I would think that even a woman who didn't like to cook would be contented in such a cozy, efficient room."

He grinned in approval of her enthusiasm, saying in a soft, melodious drawl, "That's a much more satisfying reaction."

There was as much warmth in his eyes as in his voice, and he was staring at her mouth again. Swallowing tensely, she waved her arm in an attempt to distract his attention. "I've never seen anything quite like it. Your architect is to be congratulated."

A dimple dented his left cheek as his grin widened, and he inclined his head in a modest gesture.

"You've just congratulated the architect very nicely, thank you."

She was startled by his admission and looked up at him in amazement. "You designed this house?"

"Designed and built it, from the foundations up."

"Did you hire an interior decorator?"

He gave a slight shake of his head. "No, I did all the decorating myself."

Tina didn't know why she was surprised to discover that Steven Michaels had planned his own home. He wasn't the kind of person who would trust anyone else to give him what he wanted, she realized, not when he could do so himself. From what she'd already seen, she suspected that he was a man of many talents. While following him into the kitchen she had been more aware of him than of the rooms she passed, but she had retained an impression of elegance and good taste.

There had been a game room complete with a pool table and a corner bar, and a formal dining room decorated in beige and apricot tones. Then she remembered the crystal chandelier hanging above the polished oak table, and she paused in sudden realization. It was a piece of delicate beauty amid an otherwise conventional decor, its sparkling prisms reflecting light and color like a rainbow. She wondered if he realized how much that single ornament told her about him.

For once oblivious to his presence, Tina gave her head a shake as a small smile tugged at her lips.

She had an idea he would be extremely disconcerted if he could read her mind. From the things she'd heard about him she had expected him to be callous and insensitive, a man who would view a need to surround himself with beauty as a weakness.

Although she was relieved to discover he wasn't as functionally practical as she had at first thought him to be, she was disturbed to realize how much it mattered to her.

A slight movement from the man occupying her thoughts interrupted her musings, and she shrugged her shoulders self-consciously. "I'm sorry, I was a million miles away."

"No, you weren't."

She looked at him in alarm and wondered if her expression had betrayed the fact that she'd been thinking of him. Her discomfort grew until she felt completely flustered, and she unconsciously tilted her chin in defiance. Then she stalled for time in the only way left open to her, with a question. "I . . . what do you mean?"

"I mean you were right here in your imagination, weren't you?" He leaned back against the counter and crossed his arms over his broad chest. "Do you enjoy cooking, or is it just a way to make a living?"

She exhaled the breath she'd been holding, relieved that she hadn't made a fool of herself. Then she saw that the curiosity in his gaze was genuine, and it gave her a good feeling to know he wasn't just attempting polite conversation. "Get me near a stove, and I lose all touch with reality," she confessed sheepishly. "Dennis used to call me a food freak."

"Your husband?" he asked.

She inclined her head, and her mouth curved and softened with memory. "He used to say I was at my worst when I was 'conjuring.'"

"Conjuring, like in witch's brew?"

"Exactly," she said with a laugh. "I love concocting new recipes, and when I'm in a creative mood I lose track of time. Dennis would tease me and insist that he was a deprived, neglected spouse, but he was always the first to test my culinary efforts. I used to tell him he only stayed thin by the grace of God, since he certainly didn't have much willpower where food was concerned."

Steve's expression grew pensive, as though he didn't like the direction his thoughts were taking but was helpless to divert them. "It sounds as though you and your husband had a good relationship."

She was puzzled by the inflection in his voice. "You seem disapproving."

"I sound jealous!" he exclaimed.

Her mouth opened and closed in wordless confusion. Finally she managed to squeak, "Jealous?"

"Is that so hard to understand?" he asked. "The two of you had a lot in common, didn't you?"

She nodded. "Yes, we did."

"While you and I are opposites in every respect."

"We hardly know each other," she whispered.

This time it was he who shook his head. "We knew each other the minute our eyes met, Christina."

He was going too fast for her, and her delicate features reflected the distress and confusion she felt. "I'm not here for any other reason than to cater your party, Mr. Michaels."

"As I told you before, my name is Steve, and as a mind reader you leave a lot to be desired. Right now this damned dinner is the last thing on my mind, Christina."

"Tina," she corrected automatically, too disturbed by the intensity of his expression to pay attention to what she was saying. She inhaled deeply, trying to control the unevenness of her breathing. "Everyone calls me Tina."

"Is that what your husband called you?"

She jumped at the harshness of his question, surprised into a nod of agreement. He placed gentle hands on her shoulders and straightened until they stood close together. "Then for me you'll always be Christina."

His voice was a mere murmur of sound as he looked down at her, and Tina felt anxiety twist in her stomach. The fact that he'd resolved to call her by her full name held nuances of an intimacy that was strangely shocking. She could feel his warm breath against her mouth, and trembled. Unfortu-

50

nately, her thin blouse was no protection against his tense fingers, which seemed to be imprinting a brand of possession upon her flesh.

"What does a man like you know about always?" she asked with sudden harshness. "You live alone in this huge house, and you must like it this way or you'd have done something about it long ago."

His face darkened at her words, but his response was controlled when he said, "Does my solitary state bother you, Christina?"

Yes, it bothered her to know that he was a loner, a man well satisfied with the life he'd made for himself. She sensed instinctively that he wasn't the kind of person who wanted or needed a steady, meaningful relationship. Although he might occasionally appreciate a female companion for obvious reasons, he wouldn't want to disturb the set pattern of his existence for a wife or the children they might have together.

But she wasn't like that, she thought fiercely. Her time with Dennis had shown her how good a commitment between two people could be, and someday she hoped to find another man who wanted to share her future. She intended to marry again; to have a husband and babies. Unlike Steven Michaels, she found no pleasure in the prospect of spending the rest of her life alone.

Tina felt chilled to the bone when he drew her closer to the heat of his body. There were conflicting signals in her mind, and a growing feeling of vulnerability to this man. She sensed an aching void inside of him, one that would take a strong woman to fill. Although one part of her mind urged her to flee his seductive allure, her warm, giving nature urged her to wrap her arms around him and never let him go.

Tormented by her opposing desires, Tina tried to pull herself out of his arms. But even as she struggled for freedom she heard him whisper, "I want you, Christina."

It was then she knew she'd been caught in the eagle's talons, and the knowledge terrified her. The sensual promise in his voice made her quiver with an awareness of what it would be like to die and be reborn in his embrace. But what good was rebirth, she asked herself, if she was left with a heart torn and savaged beyond repair?

"No!"

The cry was a pitiful attempt at self-defense, and he saw through her without the least difficulty. His mouth softened into a satisfied smile, a predatory gleam in his eyes. "And you want me almost as much, don't you?"

Her breasts were pressed against his chest, and when her nipples hardened in response to his claim she knew he could feel the change. His chest surged as he took in a deep, unsteady breath. She hadn't had to speak to give him his answer, and there was nothing she could do to deny her body's reaction. When his hands shifted to encircle her neck she stumbled, only then becoming aware of

52

how naturally she'd been leaning on him for support.

The realization hardened her resolve, but her voice shook when she tried to coalesce her thoughts into speech. "You're taking too much for granted."

His thumbs rubbed gently against her jawline, lingering there when her teeth clenched in determination. "I didn't come here to provide you with a playmate," she said. "You can indulge in all the casual affairs you please, but not with me."

He winced, but his somber features remained confident in his power over her. "You know you don't really believe that."

"I don't know what I believe anymore!"

Tina heard the uncertainty in her voice and was disgusted with her contrary behavior. If she couldn't be sure of her own convictions, she asked herself angrily, then how could she expect him to be? Hurriedly she sought to correct her mistake. "If you really want to know what I believe in, then I'll tell you," she said with quiet dignity. "I believe in marriage, and commitment, and children. I don't intend to share a man's bed without sharing his love, because I'd be cheating myself of all the things I consider important in life."

Immediately his features hardened, and his eyes held a brooding darkness as he mocked, "I'm impressed by your moral fiber, but I notice you don't object to indulging in a bit of emotional blackmail to get your own way. If I want you I'll have to pay the price, is that it?"

She gasped at the bitterness in his voice, appalled at the conclusions he'd drawn by her impassioned words. "That's not true, Steve. I don't want anything from you!"

"Then you're lying to yourself, honey," he said, his mouth slanted into a knowing smile. "You don't love me, but you *do* want me. Don't you think I'm experienced enough to know when a woman physically responds to me?"

Her eyes grew hostile. "Since my husband died there have been a lot of men who have wanted to take care of my physical needs."

A muscle pulsed in his jaw, his anger evident in the stiffening of his body. "Don't try to place that particular barrier between us, Christina. I'm not ashamed of wanting to make love to you, and flinging the memory of your husband at my head isn't going to make any difference."

"At least he cared about what I needed emotionally," she cried. "You don't care about anything as long as your desires are satisfied. Well, I told those other men what I'm going to tell you. I'm just not interested in compromising my principles to satisfy your temporary hunger for my body!"

"It's a hunger you share."

She was unable to deny the accusation, and she looked away from the penetrating intensity of his gaze. "You're a very attractive man, as I'm sure you've been told before."

"What other women have told me has no bearing on our relationship."

"We don't have a relationship!"

"But we will!"

He suddenly smiled, and she shivered at the sensual promise in his amber-flecked eyes.

Tina usually enjoyed the catering side of her business, but tonight had been an ordeal she wouldn't want to repeat. All evening Steve's eyes had followed her movements as she had served his guests, and when the last of his friends departed she'd breathed an audible sigh of relief. But her relief had been short lived. He entered the dining room where she was clearing off the table.

"You look exhausted," he said. "Why don't you leave that until morning?"

The tray of dishes balanced against her arm rattled, and he quickly reached out to avert disaster. Setting them down, he gave her a searching glance. "You didn't think you were leaving tonight, did you?"

"Of course I—I am," she spluttered. "The storm's almost over, and as soon as I've cleared away the last of this mess, I'll be on my way."

His face assumed a stubborn expression. "Not in that van, you won't!"

"Who gave you permission to tell me what I can do?"

"I don't need permission to stop someone from breaking their damn fool neck."

She rubbed the edge of her temple and sighed with exasperation. "I'm too tired to argue with you, Steve."

"Then don't," he said swiftly, taking her by the arm and leading her out of the room. "Since it's finally stopped raining and the wind has died down, why don't we sit out on the veranda for a while? It's stuffy in here."

Tina didn't know why she agreed so readily, she really didn't. Meekly she walked with him to the front door, telling herself that a short rest in the fresh air would help restore her energy. But the truth was not that simple, as she discovered when Steve sat beside her on the porch swing. The moment she felt his warmth against her side she knew she wasn't ready to leave him . . . not quite yet.

He'd handed her a flannel jacket from the hall closet before they stepped outside, and she drew it around her more as a protection than to shut out the cold. "Thank you for letting me use your coat," she blurted uneasily.

She saw his smile from the corner of her eye, not able to bring herself to face him. That's why she knew the instant he lifted his arm to wrap it about her shoulders, and also why she found herself chattering nonstop. "Mine takes forever to dry," she continued as she tried to ignore his hand lifting her hair from her neck, "which is dumb since it's a raincoat. Some material is like that, you know. I don't know why the manufacturer didn't take that into consideration when it was made. But it wasn't very expensive, and I—"

Her words were halted by his mouth, which brushed against hers with warm insistence. "Hush," he whispered.

"Steve, I don't want—"

Again she failed to complete her sentence, this time because of a rush of emotion that caused her toes to curl. He smiled against her lips, and his tongue emerged to taste their sweetness. "Open your mouth for me."

With a betraying sigh she did as he asked, and for long moments she savored the sensuous glide of his tongue. The kiss began as a search of discovery for both of them, but then it fueled a passion neither of them could deny. With a moan that was more of a growl, Steve turned her until she lay across his lap, his teeth sucking and biting at her lower lip when she started to protest.

"I need this," he gasped, his free hand cupping her jaw to keep her mouth under his. "Don't stop me, Christina. Just give me a few kisses, so I can taste your sweetness."

He devoured her mouth with a savage hunger, and she arched her full, throbbing breasts against his chest. Her senses were spinning out of control, every part of her body aching for the satisfaction he could give her. She gave in to his plea, unable to stop herself from wanting him. Slowly her hands slid around his neck, and at the touch of her fingers against his thick brown hair he muttered his satisfaction.

"God," he exclaimed in a shaken voice. "I never thought I'd get you alone. Let's go back into the house, where it's warm, honey. I want to touch every inch of your lovely skin."

The sensual haze clouding her mind suddenly lifted, and her hands slid to his shoulders and began to push him away. "I . . . no, Steve."

"What do you mean?" he asked, his eyes studying her with narrowed intensity. "You want it as much as I do."

She winced at the callousness of his remark, suddenly angry with him for turning a beautiful moment into something ugly and calculated. "Do you think that makes what you're contemplating right, or do you usually make love to women you don't know?"

"You're sure choosing a hell of a time to start moralizing, Christina. In case you haven't noticed, my body has gone beyond just thinking."

He didn't need to elaborate, since she could feel his hard, male pressure throbbing against her hip. Heat flooded through her at the knowledge of his arousal, but her own weakness made her angry. With a defiant toss of her head she lied, "Well, mine hasn't!"

He gazed meaningfully at the pulse that pounded against her throat, and then lowered his eyes to her heaving breasts as she fought for breath. "Like hell it hasn't!"

Suddenly all the fight went out of her, and tears began to form in her eyes. "Please," she cried like a tired child, "I want to go home."

He muttered an obscenity beneath his breath and lifted her into his arms. Then he scowled as he saw a tear trickle down her pale cheeks, his shaking head conveying his disgust with her and all females who used weeping to gain an advantage over a man. "Stop sniffling, woman. Just give me enough time to get the damn car out of the garage, and I'll take you home."

CHAPTER FOUR

"Did old Gertie break down on you again?"

Tina turned a lackluster gaze toward the open back door, where Silas was stamping mud off his boots before entering Deli-Cacy's kitchen. After Steve had dropped her off at her apartment she'd showered and gone to bed, but hadn't been able to sleep. She'd been angry enough with herself to spit nickles, and had tossed and turned for what remained of the night.

"What?" she asked absentmindedly, her mind grappling with the problems created by a six-foot-four cowboy with dark-honey eyes.

"Where's the van?"

She turned her head to the grill, where ham and bacon slices sizzled hotly. "It's still at the Michaels' place."

"How'd you and Kathy Sue get home?"

"Mr. Michaels drove me."

There was instant suspicion in the glance he threw at her. "What do you mean, he drove you? Where was Kathy Sue."

Tina shrugged, aggravated by her small slip of the tongue. Leave it to Silas to pick up on the singular reference. "She cut her hand," she replied, "so I went alone. I told her not to come in today, by the way."

She waited for the explosion with bated breath, and it wasn't long in coming. "You went . . . why in tarnation didn't you call me?"

"I didn't want to interrupt your anniversary celebration."

"As if that would have mattered!"

"It might not have mattered to you," she remarked quietly, "but I don't think Della would have felt the same."

Silas snorted angrily. "Do you think Della would place dinner and a little cuddling above your welfare?"

Tina grinned and tried to interject a lighter note into the conversation. "Do you and Della still . . . cuddle, Si?"

"I ain't that old, Miss Sassymouth, and don't be trying to change the subject."

He stomped over to hang up his coat and reached for the white chef's apron hanging on a hook against the wall. He slipped it over his head and moved to stand beside her. As he took the metal spatula out of her hand, he inspected her pale features with calculating eyes. "Did he try anything?"

She turned hurriedly so Silas wouldn't notice

her reddening cheeks, and lied for all she was worth. "Of course not!"

Slipping a mittened pot holder over her hand, she withdrew a batch of biscuits from the oven. But Silas knew her too well, and as she placed the savory bread in the warming bin he waved the spatula in her direction. "Like fun he didn't!"

"All right," she snapped, at the end of her patience. "He made mad, passionate love to me. Is that what you wanted to hear?"

She could sense his indignation. "If he forced himself on you, I'll—"

"He didn't need to use force," she responded bitterly.

Si's jaw hung slack for a moment, until a grin split his face. "Like that, is it?"

Tina sent him a furious glance from beneath her lashes. "Like what?"

"You fancy him, that's what."

"I do not," she argued automatically. "He's an irritating, bossy, opinionated, conceited, snobbish . . ." She ran out of descriptive words and continued to scowl into space.

"Sounds like true love to me," he cackled.

"The word is *lust,* Silas Porter. Pure, unadulterated lust."

"That's a part of it, right enough."

"It's the only part Mr. Steven Michaels is interested in, that's for sure."

"Give him time, Missy."

"It would be insanity to give him anything."

Silas scratched the top of his bald head, his gaze introspective. "You're right about that," he agreed. "You hold out for a wedding ring, you hear?"

"It doesn't work that way anymore." She sighed heavily. "These are the days of women's liberation, haven't you heard?"

"I've heard, all right," he muttered glumly, "and no matter what Kathy Sue thinks, I'm all for women having equal rights with men. But that don't mean a woman like you should be short-changed either."

"A woman like me is an anachronism, Si," she murmured dejectedly. "I should have been born a hundred years ago."

"Why, because you respect marriage and all it stands for?" He laid the spatula on the counter and lowered the heat on the grill. "Being liberated doesn't mean a female has to lose her ideals or her dreams for the future. You stick to your guns, so that Michaels fella can see what you're made of. He'll come around to the idea of being double harnessed, you wait and see!"

"I don't want to discuss it."

Luckily she didn't have to, because at that moment the phone rang. She practically ripped it off the wall, her voice unusually surly as she announced the restaurant's name. Then she cursed herself for her unbusinesslike attitude and asked with forced pleasantness, "May I help you?"

There was the sound of a deep, masculine chuckle. "You certainly can, honey."

"Mr. Michaels, we open for breakfast in five minutes, and I don't have time to chat. Was there a reason for this call, or are you just trying to annoy me?"

"Would I do that?"

"You certainly would."

"I'm wounded to the heart, Christina."

She drew in an exasperated breath. "You don't have a heart."

There was a moment of hesitation before he whispered, "Then why is it beating so fast?"

She closed her eyes, her own heartbeat quickening at the sensuality in his husky voice. "Why did you call, Steve?"

"To let you know I had the van towed to Charlie Spencer's."

"But they're transmission specialists," she wailed in protest. "Steve, I can't afford work like that!"

"I'll take care of it."

She caught her breath. "You most certainly will not!"

"We'll discuss it over dinner tonight."

"I'm going to call Charlie and cancel the work order."

"It's too late," he told her with irritating cheerfulness. "They've already started work on it."

"They'll stop when I tell them you didn't have my permission to take the van to them for repair. Charlie Spencer's a nice old man, but even he won't work for nothing."

"He's already been paid for his estimate."

"You—you didn't!"

Her appalled exclamation was loud enough to break his eardrum, but he didn't seem at all dismayed by her anger. "Yeah, and the guy that shares shop space with him gets it next, Christina. I've ordered him to rebuild the engine."

"Oh, God," she whispered. "I can just imagine what they're thinking."

"Does it matter?"

"Of course it matters," she screeched indignantly. "Those two eat breakfast here five days a week, and they're friends of Si's. You might as well have placed an ad in the *Nevada Union,* you calculating rat."

"We'll discuss it at dinner."

"I'm not going anywhere with you!"

He simply ignored her statement and said, "I'll pick you up at eight."

She opened her mouth to vent more of her anger, but heard the click as he hung up. With a muttered imprecation she slammed down her own receiver and stood glaring at it accusingly.

"Sounds like you're a mite upset."

"You got it in one," she said through gritted teeth.

"I take it he's having old Gertie's innards replaced."

She rubbed the back of her neck, trying to ease the tight muscles. "I'll pay him back every penny."

"I don't doubt it, but at least in the meantime I

won't have to stand with my heart in my mouth every time you drive off."

She pursed her lips and blew an errant strand of hair from her forehead. "Go on," she demanded. "Side with that oversexed cowboy."

"There ain't nothing wrong with oversexed cowboys." He grinned. "I was one myself."

She propped her hands on her hips, indignation evident in every line of her body. "Don't you say another word, Silas Porter. Not one . . . more . . . word!"

Tina slid into her jeans and looked at the clock beside her bed. It was ten minutes to seven, which meant she would have plenty of time to escape before zero hour. As she tugged a comfortably loose, gold cable-knit sweater over her rounded hips she smiled with satisfaction. She could just picture the angry scowl on Steve's face when he arrived and found that his prey had bolted.

She swept her hair back into a ponytail and muttered, "It'll serve him right."

The reflection that looked back at her from the mirror over her dresser looked plain and a bit pale, but she wasn't in the mood to put on any makeup. She had worked late at the deli and was just too tired to bother. The shower she'd taken when she arrived home hadn't made her feel any better, and she cursed having to leave when all she wanted to do was slip into her bed and seek oblivion in sleep.

With a resigned sigh she reached for her shoulder bag, leaving the temptation of her bedroom behind. She would spend a nice, relaxing evening visiting Kathy Sue, and she hoped Steven Michaels waited around long enough to starve to death. The thought of returning to find his big, hard-muscled body expired on her doorstep was curiously satisfying. She chuckled as she walked across the living room and threw open the front door.

"Will wonders never cease," drawled a mocking voice, "a woman who's ready on time."

Her head whirled around, her eyes widening at the figure casually lounging against the wall. "But you said eight o'clock."

He uncrossed his long arms, straightening to reach behind her and close the door. "Did I?"

"You know you did," she said quietly, just barely managing to keep herself from screaming at him like a fishwife.

"I assume you intended to be back by eight o'clock, then?"

She gave him a guilty glance before tilting her chin defiantly. "I never agreed to have dinner with you."

He smiled and rubbed his thumb against her pouting lips. "I didn't expect you to."

She jerked her head back, her eyes warning him to keep his distance. "Then why are you here?"

"To take you to eat."

She clenched her right hand into a fist, and he shook his head. "My nose has already been broken

67

twice. You wouldn't want to add to the damage, would you?"

"I'd like nothing better, but you'd probably hit me back."

"Never! I'm very fond of that button nose of yours, and I can think of a means of retaliation that would satisfy me more."

"I'm not worried about satisfying you."

As soon as she saw the corner of his mouth twitch she knew she'd made a drastic error in judgment. Heat spread up her neck and over her face, and she didn't know where to look when he gazed knowingly at her. "Aren't you?"

Gathering her flagging courage, she scowled up at him. "You know what I mean!"

The eyes looking deeply into hers held an unmistakable intent. "Anyway, you have nothing to worry about, Christina. You won't have any trouble satisfying me, and you know it as well as I do."

Embarrassed, Tina gave a fuming growl and headed toward the elevator, trying hard to ignore him when he followed. But he was a difficult man to ignore, as she discovered when the door slid smoothly shut behind them. The space was too small, and the man too large, for her to escape the enforced intimacy. With fatalistic dread she watched his calloused brown hand reach out to depress the stop button, halting them between floors.

"What do you think you're doing?"

She knew very well what he was doing, that was

the trouble. It didn't take the gleam in his eyes to convince her she was in a world of trouble, and she backed against the wall with stumbling haste. "You stay right where you are, Steven Michaels!"

"I've never made love in an elevator before."

"And you're not going to now, you sex fiend!"

"A sex fiend, am I?"

She scurried toward the opposite wall as he began to approach her, but he quickly blocked any further attempt to avoid him by placing his hands on either side of her head. Eventually the whole weight of his body was pressing her backward, and her legs were trembling so badly from contact with his hard thighs that she couldn't have moved to save her life. "Steve, please."

"That's what I'm going to do," he responded, his voice rife with suppressed passion. "I'm going to please you like you've never been pleased before, honey."

Her heart was pounding at an alarming rate, and she knew if she didn't quickly find a way to defuse this situation she was a goner. "My name is not honey."

He didn't pay the least attention to her objection. Instead he lowered his head until his mouth rested against the side of her neck, and he began to nibble sensuously at the fluttering pulse he discovered there. "But you are like honey, Christina," he murmured from deep in his chest. "Dark, wild honey, sweet and warm against my mouth. I was awake all night in agony, remembering the flavor of you."

She tried to evade his touch, but stopped with a gasp when her squirming caused an immediate alteration in the shape of his body. He laughed softly and ground his hips sensuously against her, forcing her to feel the change her closeness had caused.

"For goodness sake, Steve," she whispered in panic. "This is a public elevator."

When that reminder didn't work, she tried to flatter him into behaving with a little sense. "A—a man of your—your stature wouldn't m-make love in an elevator. It—it isn't respectable."

"When I'm with you I don't feel respectable." As if to emphasize his point, his tongue began doing incredible things to her ear.

She closed her eyes and moaned. When she heard the low, throaty sound of arousal she made, she wanted to rip out her vocal chords. The next moment he stopped tormenting her ear and started on her mouth. He licked her lips until they were moist and pliant, and then began sucking away the dampness like a man dying of thirst in the desert.

With the last of her fading willpower she shoved her hands against his chest, gaining an inch of distance from his marauding tongue. In real desperation she gasped, "I—I'm hungry."

"Oh, God!" he groaned. "So am I, baby."

"No, I mean I—I'm really hungry," she protested in panic. "You did promise to t-take me to dinner, Steve."

70

"You mean I have to feed you first?"

She wasn't in agreement with his exact wording, but right now she wasn't in a position to split hairs. One false move on her part, and he'd probably have her flat on her back on the damned elevator floor. Her lungs felt as though they were going to burst, but she managed to inhale enough oxygen to blurt, "Yes!"

Immediately he released her, and her eyes resembled a baby owl's at the glittering expression of triumph she saw reflected on his face. "You set me up," she hissed furiously. "All you wanted was to get me to agree to have dinner with you."

"That isn't all I want, but it's a start."

"You despicable rat, you . . ."

He arched a quizzical brow, and remarked helpfully, "Sex fiend?"

"If the boot fits, cowboy."

"Oh, it does, and I plan to wear it."

"Over my dead body, Mr. Michaels!"

"I'd prefer you alive and kicking. I never did go in for ravishing unconscious women."

"Oh, I'd be kicking, all right," she rejoined with scornful emphasis. "Right where it hurts."

He grinned unrepentantly and casually pressed the ground-floor button. Then he slipped off his jacket, his mouth curving wryly as he held it in front of himself. "If it makes you feel any better, this little exercise didn't leave me entirely unscathed. You might as well have kicked me, since I'm aching anyway."

71

She almost smiled at the boyish petulance in his voice, but refused to give him an advantage. Instead she pressed her lips primly together and dropped her eyes to the part of his anatomy that was luckily hidden by his coat. "It's no more than you deserve, you animal. I hope someone snatches your coat, and you get arrested for indecent exposure."

He choked off his booming laugh as the door to the foyer slid open. A couple of elderly women stared at his handsome, denim-clad figure in feminine appreciation before taking their place in the elevator, and as Tina and Steve stepped past them he leaned down to murmur wickedly in her ear. "You wouldn't want to have those sweet old ladies shocked, now would you?"

She gnashed her teeth together. "It would be worth it, and those sweet old ladies are looking at you like you're the ice-cream man's flavor of the month."

"I'd tell the authorities my condition was your fault, and they'd put us in the same cell. Wouldn't that be cozy?"

"Oh, shut up," she snapped, ignoring the look of stern disapproval the two women gave her.

If they were so innocently susceptible to a pretty face, she decided wrathfully, she should jerk up that jacket and see what they thought of the rest of him! In high dudgeon she crossed the carpeted lobby, trying desperately to forget what she thought of the rest of him.

* * *

Much to her surprise Steve behaved himself during their meal. There were no sexual undertones to their conversation, and eventually she felt herself relaxing in the casual comfort of a restaurant known for its chicken-fried steak. She spooned the last mouthful of peach cobbler into her mouth and leaned back with a sigh of satisfaction. "That was delicious."

"The cobbler, or that disgusting concoction smothered in country gravy you made me watch you devour?"

"Both, and no one told you to watch me," she retorted, feeling quite expansive now that her stomach was full. "Didn't your mother teach you it's bad manners to stare at people while they eat?"

To her dismay his eyes darkened as though with pain, and he uttered a harshly derisive laugh. "What would the town tramp know about manners, even if she'd been around long enough to teach me anything?"

Several seconds went by before she could manage a sound. "Your father?"

"Your guess is as good as mine, sweetness," he muttered, looking down as his finger traced the wood-grained tabletop. "My birth certificate read Steven Michael, father unknown."

There was a lump in her throat, and she had to swallow twice before she could say, "Oh, Steve!"

He suddenly lifted his head, his eyes glittering through his long lashes. "Does it matter?"

She shook her head, and reached out to still his restless hand. "No, but I think it matters a great deal to you."

He shrugged. "When I was a kid, maybe."

"Maybe?" she questioned gently.

His hand twisted beneath hers, until it was he who was doing the holding. "All right," he admitted with a cynical smirk. "It was pure hell growing up in a small town, where everyone knew you were the bastard son of the local good-time girl. Why do you think my nose has been busted so many times?"

"Who raised you?"

"My grandmother at first, but she died when I was about ten."

"That must have been hard on you."

"God, no! She was a pillar of the community before my mother shamed her. After that she lived in virtual seclusion and viewed me as the cross she had to bear in life. I was the skeleton in the family cupboard, and every chance she got she took a switch to my backside to keep me morally upright. It's no wonder my mother had to look for love in the backseat of cars," he ended woodenly. "She sure didn't find any in that house."

"I'm so sorry, Steve."

His hand tightened around hers with bruising force. "I don't want your pity, Christina. I just thought you had the right to know about me, that's all."

"Why?"

He looked startled, but his grip eased slightly. "What do you mean, why?"

"I mean why should you care what I think?" she asked in a whisper.

His eyes held hers, and she saw bewilderment in their depths. "I don't know," he admitted just as quietly. "I just do, that's all."

"Do you usually explain your background to every woman you're interested in?"

"No, but then I've never been this interested in a woman before."

Her features must have reflected disbelief, because he was quick to add, "You're different, Christina. You're what old Granny would have called a 'good woman,' and I'm inexperienced in dealing with females of your caliber."

"Haven't you ever loved anyone, Steve?"

He gave a stilted laugh. "I don't believe in it, darlin'."

She gasped, and gazed at him with sadness in her eyes. "You don't mean that!"

It wasn't a question, but he chose to interpret it as one. "People use each other and call it by a word that has no real meaning. The way I see it, we're all looking for something in a relationship, and it doesn't do a damn bit of good to wrap it up in romantic nonsense. Nothing lasts forever, no matter how many promises are made."

"Then you see it wrong, Steve."

"You were happy in your marriage, but can you honestly tell me that nothing would have ever come between you and your husband if he'd lived?" His eyes were suddenly calculating and cruel. "Another woman, perhaps?"

She flinched at his question and slowly withdrew her hand from his. "I'd like to go now."

With a stifled exclamation he got to his feet, and threw a wad of bills onto the table as he waited for her to rise. He seemed hard and unapproachable, his anger evident in the tenseness of his body. Together they walked into the street, and Tina shivered from more than the cold wind piercing her clothing. She got into the car automatically, feeling frozen inside, the pain caused by his question beating relentlessly through her mind.

"Christina, I didn't mean what I said." He muttered something she couldn't hear and burst out, "Any man in his right mind wouldn't want another woman after he'd had you."

She stared around her in surprise. They were parked in front of her apartment building, and she didn't even remember the drive. "It's all right."

"No, it isn't all right!"

She turned to look at him, and when he saw the tears in her eyes he groaned and pulled her against him. "I swear I didn't mean to hurt you, baby. Please don't look at me like that."

"Like what?" she responded dully.

His face twisted in remorse. "As if I'd shoved a knife in your heart."

"But you were right, Steve. There are no guarantees in life, not the kind you were referring to.

Who knows what would have happened between Dennis and me in the years we should have had together? Marriage has its own kind of pressures, and the people we love don't always react the way we think they will."

His arms tightened around her, and his hand cupped the side of her face as she muffled a sob against his chest. "I know, Christina. Don't let me put doubts in your mind."

"You can't know," she cried in anguish, "because you don't believe in what I felt for Dennis. When he died I wanted to die, too, because I loved him so much."

When she twisted in his arms he let her go without a struggle, his features as pale as her own in the glow of the streetlights. "But you wouldn't understand, because you've never let yourself be vulnerable to anyone, have you?"

"I'm damned vulnerable to you, Christina."

"Only because you want me," she said tiredly, "and that's just not good enough, Steve."

"It's all I can give you," he uttered harshly.

"For how long?"

"How the hell do I know?" he retorted impatiently. "You want me to tie up my feelings in a bright red ribbon and give them to you with a promise of love everlasting. But I've never learned how to care for anyone but myself, and the sooner you realize that the better off you'll be."

"I know, that's the trouble."

She felt old and tired as she opened the car door

and began to slide across the seat. When he started to open his own door she stopped him with a touch on his arm. "I don't want you to see me to my apartment."

"What you mean is you don't want to see me again, period."

His eyes held a wild glitter, and there were deep grooves beside his mouth when she said, "That might be for the best, Steve. I need love, and by your own admission you're not the man to give it to me."

He gripped the steering wheel until his knuckles whitened. "You need me, and I can give you all the loving you'll ever want."

"What you're offering I can get from any man."

"But I'm not just any man," he said, his voice holding a warning, "who's willing to let his guts be torn out by a woman. I want you, and eventually I'll make you admit that you want me just as much."

As she walked away from the car, she felt new tears begin to flood her eyes. This time her pain was caused by a man without trust; one who was too scarred by his past to believe in all the emotions that made life worth living. He was a solitary man who preferred his life the way it was. But as she listened to his car roar down the street, she was very much afraid he'd already accomplished his aim. She wanted him physically, just as much as he wanted her. The only difference was, she also wanted all the things he had vowed he could never give her.

CHAPTER FIVE

Tina didn't recognize herself in the week that followed her disastrous evening with Steve. She was tense and irritable, and her usual even temperament seemed to have disappeared. She jumped every time the phone rang at the restaurant, which it seemed to do with endless regularity. He'd already called her there three or four times. The first time she'd been abrupt and hung up on him, and spent the rest of the day and most of the night suffering pangs of guilt for her rudeness.

After that she asked Si or Kathy Sue to answer the phone, informing them that if Steve called she was too busy to speak to him. Involving them made her conscience work overtime, but at least it saved her from having to hear his deep, husky voice over the line. Eventually, though, Steve got the message, and the calls stopped.

Still, she couldn't help wondering why he hadn't tried to call her at home, until she remembered that her number wasn't listed. She told herself rather resentfully that if he really wanted to see her, he would have already shown up at her apartment. He knew her address, something she remembered with sickening panic every time the doorbell rang. Then she chided herself for her dog-in-the-manger attitude. She didn't want to hear from him, or see him, or touch him. Oh, God! She didn't think she could bear touching him again.

"Aren't you ready to go yet, honey?"

She wanted to scream at Kathy Sue and tell her not to use that particular term of endearment. It was what he called her, and she couldn't stand even that common a reminder. Honey, baby, even her own unabbreviated name, had all become flicks of a whip against her aching heart. But she didn't have the right to take out her pain and anger on Kathy Sue, who was only showing her concern. So she simply shook her head, and continued trying to make some sense out of the restaurant's monthly accounts.

Her hope that Kathy Sue would just go away died as the other woman squeezed into the cubbyhole she used as an office. It wasn't even a proper room, just a recessed area off the kitchen. That was why she waited to do her bookwork until the restaurant was closed and everyone had gone home, she thought with mounting frustration. But her friend had been fiddling around for the last half hour, reluctant to leave her alone.

Kathy Sue and Si might fight like two stags during rutting season, but they were friends for all of that. She had been prepared for him to confide her troubles to the other woman, but she hadn't been ready for the results. Si had spent the last several days giving her worried looks when he thought she wasn't looking, while Kathy Sue had begun to fuss over her like a mother hen with one chick. Between the two of them she was slowly being driven stark, raving mad!

Kathy Sue propped herself against the wall, and gave her a smile sweet enough to rot teeth. With restrained impatience Tina glanced at her and brushed away the hair that kept falling in her eyes. Then she asked, "Are you leaving?"

The gum in the older woman's mouth gave three resounding pops as she chewed, but it didn't interfere with her speech. "In a little while. I thought I'd set the tables for breakfast."

Tina sighed, her expression resigned. "Si already did that."

"Oh, yeah, I guess he did at that." Kathy Sue hesitated, a frown puckering her penciled brows. "Well, then. Maybe I'll just mix up a batch of pancake batter so we won't have to bother in the morning."

This time Tina leaned back in her chair, a small grin teasing the corners of her mouth. "You already did that, Kathy Sue."

The two bright spots of color that appeared on her cheeks couldn't be attributed to the rouge she wore. "I must be getting senile."

"That's not the trouble, and you know it."

"It is too," she retorted argumentatively. "Ei-

81

ther that or I'm getting that disease, Al's something."

"If you've got Al's something," she said with a laugh, "then Si must have it too. Don't you think I've noticed the two of you taking turns to stay here until I'm ready to leave for home?"

"What about what we've noticed?" she said indignantly. "You're eating like a darned canary, you've got dark circles under your eyes, and your nerves are shot to pieces. If I didn't know better I'd think you were in love."

Tina could feel the color drain out of her face. "Don't say that!"

Her horrified whisper seemed to linger in the air between them, and Kathy Sue's face crumpled in sympathy. "I hate to see you like this, Tina."

"Don't worry, I'll get over it."

Kathy Sue waited a moment as though to gather her courage, and then asked, "Shouldn't you word that a little differently?"

Tina hated the sulky note in her voice, but she felt rather like a guilty child beneath the older woman's penetrating stare. "I don't know what you mean."

"You're not going to get over that man by hiding, that's for sure."

All of Tina's defenses disintegrated, and she asked tiredly, "Am I that obvious?"

"To me you are, but then I've been around this old world for quite a while. I've seen troubles come and troubles go." She grinned with typical irreverence. "And most of them are male."

"He's no good for me, Kathy Sue. I know that, and yet I can't seem to get him out of my mind."

"We don't always want what's good for us."

Tina slammed the ledger closed, her expression mutinous. "That's a word Steve's fond of using. Well, telling me he wants me just isn't good enough."

"It's a part of loving."

"Not to him it isn't!"

Kathy Sue's eyes narrowed in sudden comprehension. "So that's it!"

"That's what?"

"You're comparing your feelings for Steve with what you felt for Dennis."

Tina's shock was written plainly on her face. "That's not true."

"Isn't it?" Kathy Sue asked with a disparaging grimace. "Your husband was a fine man, gentle and sweet and undemanding. He pretty much let you go your own way, while Steven Michaels strikes me as the kind of guy who would demand everything a woman had to give. It won't do you any good to deny your feelings for him because of guilt."

"What makes you think I feel guilty?" she asked hotly. "I know Dennis wouldn't have wanted me to spend the rest of my life alone, just as I would have wanted him to find happiness with someone else if something had happened to me."

"I'll tell you why you're burdened by guilt," Kathy Sue insisted. "It's because you're attracted to a man as different from Dennis as night is from day, as if you're cheating his memory in some way. Isn't that the truth?"

"I—I don't know," she whispered, the bewilderment in her eyes lending truth to Kathy Sue's assertion. "I just don't know, Kathy Sue!"

Kathy Sue laid a consoling hand on Tina's back, but her words weren't intended to offer comfort. "Well, there's one thing I do know from experience, honey. No matter how hard you try, you're never going to find happiness with someone else if you keep looking over your shoulder."

Tina drew in a shaky breath and willed herself not to cry. "Is it so wrong to want to be loved, Kathy Sue?"

"How long did you know Dennis before you knew he loved you?"

"That's not a fair comparison."

"Is any comparison fair?" Kathy Sue asked gently.

Tina thought for a moment, and sighed in confusion before answering her friend's original question. "Dennis and I worked together in a restaurant in San Francisco for quite a while before we started dating. He was the manager, and I was just a trainee cook in those days. I remember I was nervous about going out with him because he was my boss."

"You didn't want to mix business with plea-sure?"

"Something like that," she agreed with a smile.

"And after you started dating?"

Tina's brow furrowed in thought. "We must have gone out together for about six months before he asked me to marry him."

"Did he tell you he loved you?"

"Not in so many words, but I knew. . . ."

"Because he asked you to marry him you knew he loved you?"

"Well, y-yes," she stammered, wondering at the convoluted reasoning behind Kathy Sue's questions.

"Did he tell you he wanted you?"

Suddenly Tina could see what her friend was getting at, and she bristled defensively. "Dennis was too shy to make love verbally, and he respected me enough to want to wait until after we were married."

Kathy Sue's face registered her barely disguised triumph. "And Steven Michaels isn't willing to wait, is he? No, any woman with eyes in her head can see he'd be far from shy where lovemaking is concerned. Surely he can be forgiven for failing to treat you like the nervous young virgin you were when Dennis first knew you. You're a grown woman now, and he's a normal man with the same physical needs you've developed over the years."

Tina's face flooded with color. "Steve doesn't

know the difference between making love and having sex."

"Then isn't it up to you to show him?"

Tina's mouth opened, but no sound emerged. She grasped the edge of the desk until her fingers ached, and stared up at Kathy Sue in dismay. Her heart was pounding so hard she thought it might leap right out of her chest, but finally she calmed herself enough to say, "He's only interested in a temporary relationship, with no ties or commitments. I'm not setting myself up for that kind of hurt."

"Are you saying you don't really love him?"

"No, but I—"

"Because if you do care," Kathy Sue interrupted as though Tina hadn't uttered a word, "then you'll give him the same chance you gave Dennis. Give him time to learn to love you, Tina."

"But he's not like Dennis," she protested in a voice trembling with emotion.

"We've already agreed on that."

Tina sought to clarify herself. "Steve's view of women has been distorted by his past, Kathy Sue. He doesn't trust women, he made that more than obvious. He sees our relationship in purely physical terms."

"Is that so wrong?"

Tina gasped in disbelief. "Are you suggesting that I become his mistress, to be discarded when he tires of me?"

"No one can make that choice for you, Tina,"

she said firmly. "If a man decides he's tired of a woman, a marriage certificate isn't going to stop him from taking off. Divorces are easy to come by these days, which is one thing I've learned from experience."

She turned to leave, but stopped with a last bit of advice. "Just remember one thing, okay? Learning to trust someone else with our happiness is difficult, and not always wise. But without trust and a willingness to take risks, no relationship is going to develop strong roots. You couldn't protect yourself from the pain of losing your husband, any more than I could stop mine from walking out on me."

Tina sat frozen as Kathy Sue left for home, the words she'd spoken reverberating in her mind. She remembered the title of a book she'd once read, and whispered it aloud. "Nobody ever promised me a rose garden."

No, she thought with a smile, that was the kind of promise no one could demand from life. She hadn't demanded it from Dennis, and she'd known both happiness and pain with him. As she got to her feet she felt a confidence born of decision. There was also fear, but she pushed it to the back of her mind. Right now all she needed to concern herself with was nurturing the roots of this new, uncertain relationship.

Pausing by the window that overlooked the courtyard in back, Tina noticed the stark, leafless branches of a weathered oak. She'd been like that tree, stripped of all adornment in the cold chill of winter. But soon spring would come, and it would bloom with new beauty. That was the cycle of life, the only real promise for the future.

As she gazed at that gnarled symbol of nature's strength and endurance, she experienced a warmth that needed no explanation. It was as though the cold despair enclosing her heart had suddenly become a flame in the midst of winter, and she caught her breath in startled wonder. Perhaps someday a beautiful garden would result from her feelings for Steve, or maybe she'd be left with a wasteland of unfulfilled dreams. She only knew that she had to try, for both their sakes.

The drive home seemed endless, as did the hours she spent getting ready to confront Steve with her decision. She took a calming bath rather than a shower, and washed and blow-dried her hair until it formed a fragrant halo around her face. Although she seldom wore much makeup, tonight she felt a need to pull out all the stops. Her hand trembled as she applied eyeshadow and mascara, the eyes that looked back at her in the mirror large and sparkling with expectation. She certainly didn't need blusher, she decided, replacing the case in her makeup bag with a grimace. The rosy color in her cheeks was already embarrassingly revealing of her emotional state.

When the doorbell pealed she gritted her teeth in frustration and decided to ignore it. She had a hunch it was Kathy Sue, coming to apologize for reading her the riot act. Her brow furrowed in indecision as she stared at the jumbled clothing piled on her bed. She couldn't decide how to dress, whether to appear coolly sophisticated or casually comfortable. What did a woman wear to visit a potential lover, anyway? She bit down on her lower lip, certain only of one thing. She didn't want to be too obvious in case he'd changed his mind about wanting her.

The bell rang again, this time being pushed longer and with more insistence. Her bedroom door was open, and she frowned impatiently in the direction of the sound. Probably Kathy Sue's conscience was giving her hell, and she'd stand in the corridor all night if she wasn't allowed inside. Tina slipped on her long flannel robe with a resigned sigh, zipping up the front as she prepared to greet her friend with a semblance of a warm welcome.

But it wasn't Kathy Sue who pushed past her the moment she opened the door. Whoever she'd expected, it wasn't the gruff, scowling man who turned to gaze at her with hostile eyes. His voice was deliberately mocking as he said, "You can close the door, honey. I'm not going to jump on you."

"You could have fooled me."

She did as he asked, glad of its support as she leaned against it, her knees suddenly wobbling beneath her. When he showed no inclination to explain his unexpected appearance, she blurted uneasily, "Why are you here?"

His eyes seemed to darken as he studied her from the tips of her bare toes to the top of her head. "Why do you think?"

She was in no mood to play guessing games, her emotions too raw at the moment for rational thought. "From the way you're looking at me, I'd say strangulation wouldn't be far off the mark."

Then she swallowed nervously and uttered a rather weak laugh. "Either that or you've changed your mind and decided to break my nose."

"As you know, I really am a bastard." He snorted with marked derision. "But I don't go around bashing women's noses."

Shocked at his self-assessment, Tina snapped, "Don't you dare call yourself a bastard, Steven Michaels."

A grim smile curved his mouth. "Isn't that why you've been avoiding me?"

She was appalled and hurt by the accusation. "Is that what you really believe, that I'm so shallow that I'd turn against you because you don't know who your father was?"

"What the hell else am I supposed to think?" he demanded. "I spill my guts about my past, and you're suddenly too busy to even speak to me on the phone."

She slammed her hands on her hips. "Did you ever think I might have been avoiding you because you scared the life out of me?"

"Don't give me that hogwash, Christina, You're a grown woman, not some untried schoolgirl."

Deep lines bracketed his mouth, making him look tired and defeated. "You couldn't bring yourself to tell me the truth, so you took the easy way out."

She shook her head. "You're crazy, Steve."

"I was crazy to believe you were different. You're just like every woman I've ever known. So gentle and caring, with eyes that seem to offer me the world until you decide that I fall short of your standards. At least my grandmother was honest, she hated me and never let me forget it. After she died I was shoved from one relative to another, each of them promising to love me until it was time to hand me over to someone else. You were right to let me down now instead of later, Christina. Because if a love with hidden conditions is the kind you're always spouting off about, then a man's better off without it!"

As Steve talked the red haze in front of her eyes deepened, until she felt nothing but a blind rage consuming her. Unaware of her actions, she marched up to him and grabbed the front of his cashmere sweater in both hands. It was a goldish-brown color, and even in her fury she noticed how well it matched his eyes. That was one reason he was able to make her angrier than she'd ever been in her life. He had so much to offer a woman—looks, intelligence, a strength to lean on in times of trouble—and yet he thought she had been turned off by his lack of a family pedigree!

The sound of his throat clearing released her from the throes of an almost blinding rage.

"Ummm, that sweater cost rather a lot, Christina."

She blinked, only then aware of the way her fingers were twisting the soft fabric. "To hell with your sweater!"

But even as she spoke she began absently to smooth the plush material across his chest. She felt his hard, rounded muscles bunch up and ripple beneath her touch, and her mind spun at the thought of sliding her palms over his bare, warm flesh. His scent was evocative of soap, Old Spice after-shave, and pure, unadulterated masculinity. She wondered if he would taste as good as he smelled.

She came to her senses abruptly, glaring up at him with eyes that flashed fire. That she could go all weak minded and feminine at a time like this made her madder than ever, and with a moue of distress she grabbed for the collar of his dark leather jacket. She wanted to shake the life out of him!

She soon discovered that shaking a man of Steve Michaels' build was like trying to teach an elephant ballet. Her ineffectiveness didn't do much to settle her temper, which was running hot and heavy. Instead she began to prod him with an accusing finger, slightly gratified when he began to back away as she continued to tell him off.

"We all come into this world the same way, you big oaf," she yelled, "bare-assed naked and squalling. Some of us are luckier than others, but it's what we do with our lives that counts in the end."

"Yes, ma'am."

His sudden meekness surprised her, and she glanced up at him with suspicion. "Are you trying to be funny?"

Tina's finger bounced off his chest when he sucked in a hearty breath. She found his whispered "I wouldn't dare" extremely satisfying.

With renewed energy she stalked him the way a mama cat teaches her kittens to hunt. Although preoccupied, she wasn't too far gone to realize that she was pushing him through her bedroom door. "And another thing," she continued with unabated wrath. "How dare you come here when I'd already made up my mind to go to you?"

A light entered his eyes, making them glow the color of whiskey in a crystal glass. "You were coming to me?"

"Yes, you jackass."

"Is that why you look so gorgeous?"

She gestured to the faded fabric of her robe. "In this old thing?"

"I assume that you were going to get dressed first."

"Of course I was going to dress," she said indignantly. "You're the one who goes around just begging to be arrested for indecent exposure."

His mouth twitched, but his features remained impassive. "Then it's a good thing you're not going to throw me out. It's damn cold out there, and I'm not about to use my coat as a shield again."

She looked down and nearly choked. Yes, he certainly would die of exposure or get himself arrested if she kicked him out now. "With my luck you'd shock those two old ladies downstairs into respiratory arrest, and I'd be the one charged with their demise for letting you loose."

With languid ease he began to study her own respiratory system, and she felt her breasts swell with an indecent amount of eagerness. The muscles rippled in his throat when he swallowed, and his voice was hoarse as he asked, "Do you have anything on under that robe?"

"Don't try to change the subject," she ordered, her tone suddenly less adamant.

He watched the rapid rise and fall of her chest. "Are you having respiratory arrest?"

Tina ignored his query, and a frown creased her forehead as she tried to remember where she'd left off before being distracted. "You spoiled everything," she exclaimed petulantly. "I wanted to see the skylight over your bed."

"Because I sure as hell am!"

She had lost the drift of their argument. "What?"

"I said you take my breath away, woman."

Pleasure shone in her eyes. "I do?"

His hand reached out, and he began to play with the zipper on the single garment that covered her nakedness. "You didn't answer my question," he reminded her softly. "Do you have anything else on under here?"

She gave him a boldly inviting smile. "That's for me to know and you to find out, Mr. Michaels."

The zipper moved one inch, and then two. "I don't think my blood pressure can stand the suspense."

He did have rather a lot of color in his face, and Tina's conscience wouldn't condone further delay. With a muttered imprecation she pushed against his chest and he sat down, the bed bouncing under his weight. For a moment he looked startled, and then a slow, sensuous smile curved his mouth. "I thought you were scared off by *my* aggressiveness."

"I'm not afraid of you, big man."

"Well, you're making me shake in my boots."

"Then take them off."

He bent forward and quickly did as she ordered. He shoved his socks inside and placed the boots together in front of the nightstand. Then he stared up at her with blatant desire and whispered, "What do you want me to take off next, honey?"

CHAPTER SIX

Steve's question rocketed through her brain, inspiring a wealth of possibilities. Gooseflesh popped out all over her body, and she curled her toes into the carpet to steady herself. She suddenly felt six years old again, back in the tall weeds of the vacant lot on the corner where she'd played doctor with Johnny Parker.

The tip of her tongue peeked out to moisten her suddenly dry lips. "Y-you can take off your jacket."

"Yes." He slipped the garment from his shoulders. "It is getting a little warm in here."

"You're telling me," she muttered.

Apprehension gripped her stomach muscles in a vise, and she stood rooted to the spot. He looked so impossibly . . . male. She shivered, her widening eyes interlocking with his like two parts of a puzzle. But then he grinned with wicked enjoyment, and she regained a little bit of her flagging confidence. With a shaking hand she gestured toward his sweater, afraid she might stammer if she tried to verbalize her wishes.

Before she had time to blink, the sweater joined his jacket on the floor, and she forgot how to breathe. Like an Adonis cast in bronze he stood there, all sculpted muscle and warm, inviting flesh. Silky brown hair curled across his broad chest, arrowing down past his hard stomach to disappear inside his slacks.

That's as far as she got before her attention was distracted by the clothing she'd been rummaging through before he arrived. Everything was still piled haphazardly at the foot of her bed, and her hands itched to restore order out of chaos. Then she sneaked another glance at his face and decided this was definitely not the right time to tidy up the mess.

He caught her furtive stare and leaned back on his hands with his long legs sprawled open. "Why don't you come a little closer?"

His husky voice danced along her nerves like a cello played by a maestro, and ripples of sensation tingled up and down her spine. She was amazed at how right he looked in her room, on her bed. For the first time she realized how much loneliness this apartment represented for her. After Dennis's death she had moved here from their little house on its acre of land, telling herself she needed to be closer to the restaurant for convenience.

But in truth she had been escaping from broken dreams and memories that were too painful to face alone. She studied Steve through the prism of time, and everything she was or had ever hoped to be suddenly coalesced in her mind. She wondered if she could begin to build the foundation of a new tomorrow with him. With a surge of joyousness she realized that dreaming was the first step.

Yet she distrusted the happiness beginning to form inside her, unsure that she could ever fully share herself with this man. His face held a strength sculpted by the blows life had dealt him, while hers held the fear of inadequacy. Together they were a portrait of contrasts, his darkness to her light, her softness to his hardness. She wondered if there would ever come a time when they would blend together to form a perfect whole.

There was an anticipatory gleam in his eyes when he said, "Come here to me, Christina."

It was both a plea and a demand, and she could no longer resist the urging of her own desire. With inner trepidation she forced herself to take one step, and then another. She felt his thigh muscles tighten when she moved between them, and she closed her eyes when he reached up to help her out of her robe. She thought she felt his hands tremble, but she was shaking so badly herself that she couldn't tell where he started and she left off.

His breath rasped sharply in his lungs. "Sweet Lord, you're lovely!"

She shivered at the passion in his voice, pleased, yet frightened to think that he might not mean the words. She felt almost paralyzed with shyness, but she needed to see his face to discover the truth. Barely slitting one eye open, she saw the genuine avidity of his gaze. His eyes were slowly studying every inch of her exposed flesh, and she wondered how she compared with other women he'd known. Compared, hah! She guessed they had all been sleek, sophisticated, and gorgeous. Suddenly she felt sick with inadequacy.

He had just told her she was lovely, but she knew she was far from beautiful. Were his words just a standard phrase he used to relax a woman he intended to make love to? The question made her miserable, and more self-conscious than she'd ever been in her life. Her breasts were high and firm, but did he think them too large? She had a small waist, but were her hips curved enough for him to find them pleasing?

Just when she thought she'd drive herself crazy with the doubts tumbling one after another in her mind, he uttered a low groan. Her lashes lifted in amazement, and what she saw effectively deprived her of what little composure she had left. There was a nerve twitching in his cheek, and his teeth were clenched so tightly together he almost seemed angry. But it wasn't anger she saw expressed in those golden eyes of his, it was a hunger so raw she began to burn from her head to her cramped toes.

Tina suddenly knew that she was not ready for this . . . no way was she going to be able to give herself to a man who expected so much from her.

99

She was gauche and uncertain, while he was assured and knowledgeable. Just because she was only a year and six-eighths short of thirty didn't mean that she could fulfill his need for her. What a fool she had been to think she had the kind of experience that would satisfy him.

In a panic borne of cowardice she wondered what he would do if she tried to make a run for it, but she didn't have a chance to find out. With a hoarse cry he pulled her down on top of him, and a gurgle of nervous laughter escaped from her throat when he whispered, "Be gentle with me."

She tried to push herself away from the intimacy he'd precipitated, but her hands got tangled in the hair on his chest. Accidentally one nail raked a button-hard nipple, and his sibilant moan was warm in her ear. Turning his head, he took the lobe of her ear into his mouth and began a rhythmic suckling. She went rigid, but she could gain no leverage with her legs dangling over the side of the bed. An exquisite sensation speared from her ear to the very tips of her breasts.

"Steven?"

"Hmmm?"

With a final, gentle scouring of his teeth he moved his mouth to another, even more sensitive area just beneath her tingling earlobe. "I—I haven't had dinner yet."

"You are not hungry, Christina."

"I'm not?" she questioned faintly.

"No, unless it's for me."

She couldn't dispute that, so she tried a different tack. "Would you believe me if I said I was thirsty?"

His entire body shook from the force of his amusement, but his reply was brief. "No!"

She sighed and tilted her head to make it easier for his foraging mouth to reach her neck. "I didn't think so."

He made a noise low in his throat. "You're chicken."

"I am not!" she denied hotly as she punched him in the arm.

"Ouch, that hurt!"

She evaded his mouth long enough to glare at him. "You deserved it for making fun of me."

"I wasn't making fun, I was stating a simple fact," he replied. "If you shake any harder we're both going to fall out of this bed."

"We're practically on the floor anyway."

His teeth gleamed whitely at her logic. "Is that what's bothering you, honey?"

She sounded as disgruntled as she felt when she muttered, "What makes you think I'm bothered?"

His large frame shook again, and he seemed to be having a great deal of difficulty articulating. "Just a foolish thought."

"Well, I'm not!" She winced at the snappishness of her reply.

"Are you certain?"

"Of course I am!" She was pleased with the lofty manner she achieved, but the effect was somewhat

101

spoiled by the air whistling from her lungs. She sounded like a ninety-year-old jogger, she decided in disgust. "Why?"

"I thought you might prefer doing it on the floor."

She had a vivid mental picture of herself sprawled on the carpet, and heat exploded in her stomach like molten lava. He was crouched between her thighs, and she was taking him inside. . . . The groan that burst from her was embarrassing enough without the hot tide of color that accompanied it.

With a murmur of distress she hid her face against his shoulder and wailed, "I can't do it at all!"

"I know."

At first she thought she'd imagined his resigned whisper, until he repeated it. "I know you can't, honey."

She jerked in his arms, and her words were muffled against his warm skin when she asked, "You do?"

"Why do you think I still have my pants on?"

With a cry of outrage she slid to her feet, forgetting her nakedness in righteous indignation. "You were playing me along to see how far I'd go!"

He folded his arms behind his head and grinned up at her. "I knew how far you'd go soon after you pushed me into the bedroom."

She slammed her clenched fists against her hips, and her chin tilted with pride. "I am not that kind of a tease, Mr. Michaels. I had every intention of—"

"Going all the way?"

His soft interruption caused her to cringe in mortification, but she couldn't back down now. With a toss of her hair she hissed, "Of course."

Before she could guess his intention, he was on his feet. She backed away with as much dignity as she could muster. "But now I've ch-changed my mind."

"Come here, Christina."

Her mouth formed a mutinous pout, but her insides were quivering like a dish of Jell-O. "No."

Then he bent down, standing up with her robe hanging from one finger. "Don't you want this?"

Feeling hunted, she looked from him to the garment he held, her self-consciousness increasing as she saw his mouth curve in a mocking smile. She tried to cover herself with her hands, but there was no way she could escape his gaze. "You are not a gentleman."

"No, I'm not, and quit trying to hide yourself from me like that."

He suddenly seemed angry, but there was another look in his eyes she couldn't interpret. "Why are you yelling?" she asked.

"Because I'm suddenly feeling as guilty as hell," he exclaimed loudly. "I didn't mean to humiliate you, so will you just come here and put this thing on before I lose my patience entirely?"

This time she couldn't move toward him fast

enough, and she almost crumpled with relief when the robe was shoved over her head and zipped as high as it would go. "Thank you," she managed to say eventually.

"For God's sake, Christina!"

With rough attention he lifted her hair where it had gotten caught inside the neckline of her robe, his eyes filled with frustration, avoiding her gaze.

"What did I say?"

"You can punch me or spit in my eye, but you have nothing to thank me for."

Her chin dropped to her chest, while her stomach lurched with sudden nausea. She had been right all along. Now he was feeling guilty because he hadn't been able to bring himself to make love to her. As a femme fatale she was a washout, but that came as no surprise. She was way out of her league with Steven Michaels, and she'd been an idiot to think she could ever be anything else.

She must have imagined that hungry look he'd given her, and he was trying to let her down gently. Gently, hah! If feeling as though a two-ton truck had been dropped on her was gentle, she'd hate to come up against him when he got rough! Then again, she hadn't been the most responsive partner he'd ever had. She could hardly blame him for being turned off by her dithering ineptitude.

Of course, there was another explanation for tonight's fiasco, one that hurt so much she wished she'd never thought of it. But once the suspicion entered her mind, it wouldn't be dislodged. Had revenge been his real motive for coming here? She sniffed, but was damned if she was going to cry in front of him. She'd already made enough of a fool of herself to satisfy his wounded ego!

He filled his hands with her hair and squeezed so tightly she was glad she couldn't feel the pressure. "Christina, I . . ."

When she lifted her head, the words he had started to say died. For endless seconds they stood there, the emotional barrier between them so strong it could be felt. Slowly he released her hair, and with a string of curses he marched out of the room. After a moment she followed him, her eyes resentful as she watched him pace furiously.

"Just what is your problem?" she asked with asperity. "It was you who decided to get even, not me. I'm the one who should be furious."

"I didn't come here to get even," he shouted, turning to face her. "I came here to convince you that you wanted me in spite of my illustrious family tree!"

"You what?" she screeched.

"I came here to seduce you, dammit!"

"Then why didn't you?"

"Because you told me a few home truths, and when I realized how wrong I was I felt like a worm."

"Then why didn't you say so?"

"You didn't give me a chance."

He began to pace again, and she watched the muscles rippling in his back with an avid fascination that nonetheless made her disgusted with herself.

"You were telling me off royally," he said, "and I couldn't get a word in. Then you started shoving me toward that damn bed, and I wanted to be there with you so badly I hurt all over."

"If you wanted me, then why . . . ?"

He whirled around to confront her. "Why didn't I finish what you'd started?"

She nodded, and he moved slowly across the room. He stood hesitantly in front of her, then gently cupped her burning cheeks in his large hands. "Because I took one look in your eyes, and knew it was all an act of bravado."

She lowered her gaze to his mouth, taking a deep breath before admitting, "It wasn't all an act, Steve. I—I wanted you too."

His lips softened into a tender smile. "I knew that, which is precisely why I held back."

"I don't understand."

His hands slid to her shoulders, and he gave her a little shake. "When I told you about my past you tried to show me compassion. Could I reward your honesty tonight with any less?"

His confession made Tina stamp her foot with impatience. "The only reward I wanted tonight was you, you overgrown ape!"

He tried to stifle a laugh but wasn't very successful. Shaking his head, he grinned at her with smug superiority. "You were *not* shaking in the throes of passion, sweetness."

106

"I was too." When she saw the skepticism on his face, she amended guiltily, "Well, maybe not every single second."

"I don't go in for half measures."

He studied her face for a moment. He was certainly doing terrific things for her morale, she thought wryly.

She assumed a haughty stance, a difficult move since he was still gripping her shoulders. Then she pointed toward the front door, her manner frigid as she muttered, "So I was right all along, and all this blather about compassion and honesty is just your way of salvaging my pride. Well, you may leave this half measure anytime you like, Mr. Michaels."

His response to her invitation was hearty and precise. "I don't like."

"Why not, since I've obviously failed your sexual requirements."

He gave her a dark glance from beneath lowered lids. "What do you think I do, go around with a barometer reading hot and cold stuck up my nose?"

"I can think of a better place for you to stick it."

"From someone who expects gentlemanly behavior from me, that is not a ladylike remark."

"So I'm no lady, surprise, surprise!"

"No, you're a spitting she-cat and you are playing hell with my self-control. Now, if you don't shut up and let me explain, I'm going to dump you back on that bed and trim your claws."

She shrugged with assumed nonchalance. "Why waste your time?" she asked. "You already tried once, and you certainly didn't like the results."

"I was enchanted by everything we did in there, Christina. Every damn . . . single . . . thing!"

Her mouth twisted with unaccustomed cynicism. "Spare me the platitudes, Steve. My ego isn't nearly as delicate as yours."

"If I hadn't given in to unbearable provocation and stripped you naked, we wouldn't be having this conversation."

"If you hadn't I wouldn't feel like a fool."

"You weren't behaving foolishly."

"That's debatable," she said with an arched brow. "Anyway, I thought knocking me down a peg or two was the point of the exercise."

He bared his teeth in frustration. "Will you get it through your head once and for all that I had no ulterior motives, Christina."

"I noticed you weren't in any hurry to drop your own pants." Renewed humiliation caused her voice to wobble ignominiously, and the pain in her eyes made him flinch.

"That was the only way I could keep my sanity," he said after a slight pause. "If I hadn't kept that material between us I would have lost control with you."

"That isn't true, you . . ." She drew in a deep breath, trying desperately to regain control over her voice. "You only wanted to make a fool of me;

to punish me because you thought I'd rejected you."

"Punish you? That's the last thing I'd ever want to do." He pulled her against his tense body and her desire to fight him grew, but she was too emotionally drained to do more than make a token resistance. It seemed the final straw, and a sob escaped her. Another followed, and soon she was crying with a hearty gusto she deplored. Her small hands somehow ended up around his neck, her fingers locked together with convulsive force.

He whispered the kind of words one would use to soothe a distraught child, and lifted her to carry her across the room. His tenderness caused her resentment to grow out of all proportion. It was his fault she was behaving childishly, she told herself. Even at her husband's funeral she had managed to suppress her grief until she was alone.

Yet here she was acting like a two-year-old, and the realization bolstered her determination. She hadn't needed anyone in a long time, and if he thought he could make a marshmallow out of her, he could think again. She was used to going it alone, and would continue on that way even if it killed her. He could just take himself off, and good riddance!

When he sat down in an overstuffed armchair, settling her securely upon his lap, she decided it was time to get a grip on herself. Nothing was going to be gained by dragging this on any longer.

All she wanted at the moment was to escape from the pain of her own thoughts.

"Let me go, Steve."

His tightening arms wouldn't let her slip away, and his voice sounded as shaken as hers had been when he murmured, "No, Christina. Just stay here and let me hold you for a little while."

Eventually she calmed down enough to look up at him. There was so much pain in his eyes that he seemed to be almost . . . tortured. She couldn't bear to see him this way. In an instant her heart heard what her mind had been denying, and the anger she'd felt drained suddenly away.

Timidly she reached up, wanting to wipe away the misery she saw on his face. "You really are sorry for what happened, aren't you?"

His mouth twisted bitterly at her surprise. "Sorry can't begin to describe the way I feel, Christina. I didn't mean to let things go that far, but I couldn't help myself. I wanted you so much, needed to be a part of you more than I've ever needed anything in my life before."

Her pale features still expressed a lingering doubt. "That wasn't the impression you gave."

"Honey, we both know I could have coaxed you into fully responding to me. I don't know exactly when it happened, but somewhere between here and your bedroom I developed a conscience. Suddenly what you wanted mattered more to me than my own selfish desires, and I couldn't stand the thought of disappointing you."

"But that's what *I* was thinking." Her whispered words held bemused comprehension. "I was afraid *you* were disappointed with *me.*"

"Why in hell would you think such a thing?" he demanded in frustration. "God, you had me so turned on I had about as much control as a boy with his first woman!"

"You . . ." She hesitated, and averted her eyes from his face. "You really did think I was lovely?"

"The loveliest woman I've ever seen," he said sincerely, his eyes glazing with memory. "I wanted to bury myself inside of your warmth, make you cry out my name as I pleasured you. But it seemed wrong for our first time together to happen because of anger and misunderstanding."

He pressed his head against the high back of the chair and closed his eyes. "I'll never forgive myself for making you doubt both me and yourself. No matter how hard I try, I can't seem to do anything right with you."

She snuggled against him, loving his warmth. "You're doing something very right at the moment."

"Then that's a first," he retorted. "From the beginning I've tried to rush you into a relationship you weren't ready for, but if it makes you feel any better, I've paid for my mistakes in ways you can't begin to imagine."

Feeling bolder by the second, she pressed her mouth to the tense line of his jaw. "I'm ready now, Steve."

"No, you're not," he argued with a resigned growl. "With any other woman I wouldn't give a damn, but with you I want it to be right when we make love."

Her heart leapt and she hid a secret smile against his chest as she questioned softly, "Why?"

There was a harassed tone in his reply. "I just do, that's all."

"Steve?"

When he didn't answer she tugged on a strand of his chest hair. He gave a satisfying yelp, and asked, "What?"

She ached to say, *I love you,* but knew he wasn't ready to accept that from her yet. From what he'd said, those words had been spoken to him before, and he had learned not to believe in them. He was a man who needed to be shown that he could trust in her feelings for him. She could only do that by example. So instead of baring her heart she simply asked, "Can we be friends?"

He stiffened, looking at her warily. "Instead of lovers?"

"How about friends first, and then lovers?"

Air exploded from his lungs in a burst of sound. "Hell! You had me scared there for a minute, Christina. Nobility isn't my style, and I don't know how long I can keep my hands off you."

She ran caressing fingers across his naked shoulder. "Me too. But let's try it for a couple of months."

"All right. I suppose that's the most I can ask

for right now, but I suspect you have a lot more willpower than I do," he remarked dryly.

She sat up with a sigh. "I guess it's pretty obvious I've never had any lovers besides my husband."

He nodded, understanding in his gaze. "That's why we'll wait until you're comfortable with the idea. And when you are, then you'll come to me. I'll be waiting."

She looked down and twisted her hands together in her lap. "Have you had a lot of lovers?"

"I've never had a lover, Christina."

She jerked her head up in shock, wanting to slug him when he corrected with a laugh, "A lot of sexual partners, yes."

She grinned and admitted ruefully, "That's what I get for being nosy."

Then his features sobered, and he reached out to still her restless fingers. "Will you do something for me, honey?"

He waited for her nod of compliance before continuing. "Promise me you won't ever again pretend to be something you're not. The women I've known over the years couldn't hold a candle to you, not in any way. You're so beautiful I melt inside when I look at you, and I only wish I could match your innocence. I know I'm not good enough for you, but I'm too damn selfish to leave you alone. I . . . don't let me hurt you, Christina."

She knew why he'd ended his sweet declaration

with a warning, but it didn't make any difference. She would take her time and when she went to him, it would be right for both of them. He might never be able to accept all that she wanted to give him, but they could only take their relationship one day at a time. For now all she could do was give him the reassurance he needed, and with a broken cry she threw herself against him.

"You won't hurt me, Steve."

Even as she whispered the words, she prayed they were true.

CHAPTER SEVEN

"If you rub that counter any harder, you're going to strip the finish."

Tina looked up at the sound of Silas's grumbling voice. "Don't you know better than to bother a woman when she's thinking?"

"Daydreamin', more like."

"So what?" She countered her sarcasm with a grin. "It's a beautiful day for dreaming."

"Since it's thirty-six degrees out there and dropping, it's a good thing we don't have a party scheduled for tonight. My bunions are killing me."

She shook her head in protest. "But there isn't a cloud in the sky."

The elderly man simply gave her a sage look from beneath his bushy eyebrows and continued to fill the salt shakers. She should know better than to contradict him by now, she thought with amusement. After all, nearly every old-timer in Nevada City gauged the weather by Si's bunions. When they were "killing him" it meant snow, "a mite persnickety" called for rain, and "fair to middlin" promised warmth and sunshine. He was extremely proud of his forecasting ability, and doubting him was like trying to give a skunk a bath.

"You just wait and see," he said. "The ground will be white as the feathers on a duck before morning."

She couldn't let that one slide by, and remarked with wide-eyed innocence, "But not all ducks are white, Si."

All she got for her pains was a "Humph," before he asked, "Isn't Steve supposed to get back tonight?"

A smile lighted her entire face. "He'd better be on his way, or I'll wring his neck. This past week has to have been the longest in recorded history."

"Missed him a bit, did you?"

She agreed, her voice soft with longing. "Just a bit."

There was a poignant silence as she once again escaped into a world that held only her and the man she loved. For nearly two months she and Steve had been together every chance they got, trying to build a relationship, trying to learn to be friends first, and eventually lovers. But their time together wasn't nearly enough to suit either of them. Both the Thanksgiving and Christmas seasons were busy ones for the deli, and it was difficult for Steve to take too much time away from the ranch.

He'd wanted her to move in with him, because of the physical distance, which made it almost impossible for them to see each other. As Steve had pointed out so many times, how could they get to know each other if they hardly spent time together? Just before he'd left for Kentucky he had once again urged her to think about living at the ranch, and the separation had done what all his arguments had failed to accomplish. She had missed him more than she would have believed possible, and tonight she was going to give him an early Christmas present.

Her heart leapt at the thought of the mental commitment she'd made during these last, interminable days. She wanted him so much, and had tried to tell him in every way she could that the time was now right for them. But he had been determined to give her some space, which hadn't been easy on either of them. She had been able to hide her frustration these last two weeks, but Steve was becoming increasingly edgy and short tempered. The physical attraction they felt for each other was stronger than ever, and she'd been amazed and touched at his restraint.

All that would change after this evening, and she shivered with anticipation. The key he'd given her to his house was in her purse, and his ranch foreman was probably right at this moment in Steve's living room setting up the large pine tree they'd chosen together yesterday. The frivolous piece of satin and lace she'd bought for the occasion was already folded in the suitcase she had waiting in the van.

When Si loudly cleared his throat to remind her that she wasn't alone, she gave him a sheepish grin and apologized.

"I should be used to it by now." He gave a sigh of resignation, but there was a merry twinkle in his blue eyes. "You been doing a lot of that lately."

Her skin took on a rosy flush, and she lowered her eyes in embarrassment. Taking pity upon her, he asked, "Did Steve get that stallion he was bidding for?"

She laughed, remembering his disgruntled voice on the phone last night. "He did, but according to Steve he was taken to the cleaners."

"Never know how an auction's going to turn out, especially in Louisville."

"Speaking of auctions," Kathy Sue interjected as she threw the dead bolt on the front door, "you should see the antique coatrack I picked up in Roseville last week."

"Knowing you, it's probably a fake."

Kathy Sue's hackles rose at Si's taunt. "Do you think I'd give my best friend a fake for Christmas?"

Silas groaned and rolled his eyes. "If it's for Della, I suppose you'll be wanting me to refinish it."

Kathy Sue's saccharine smile was accompanied by a few seconds of furious gum-popping. "Since she's your wife, you might as well do it before Christmas as after, you lazy old goat."

Si glowered, and Tina quickly interrupted the

118

fledgling argument before the two had a chance to really get going. She plastered a cheerful smile on her face and gazed at them meaningfully. "Won't it be lovely if we have a white Christmas this year? It doesn't snow often enough to suit me."

"That's true enough." Si nodded and scratched the bridge of his nose. "Some years we don't get any at all."

Deprived of her favorite pastime, namely annoying Silas Porter, Kathy Sue mumbled under her breath. "Wet, slushy gunk."

Tina could almost see the retaliation trembling on Si's lips. If he called Kathy Sue an "old biddy" one more time today she might lose the best waitress in town. With that thought in mind she jumped in with a timely reminder before Si could open his mouth. "Hey, you two, this is the season of love and goodwill toward men."

They stared at her with blank expressions, until Kathy Sue spoiled the effect with a snicker. "You're in season, right enough."

Si's belly laugh assaulted Tina's burning ears. "Will you two stop teasing me?"

In accord for once, her two employees grinned at each other. "Will you look at her face?"

Kathy Sue responded with gleeful relish. "She's as red as a firecracker. Better keep the matches away from her, Si. She's likely to explode."

Tina's eyes threatened dire retribution, but she managed to say meaningfully, "In case you haven't noticed, it's quitting time."

Kathy Sue got the message quickly enough and wiped the smile from her mouth. But Si kept on laughing, slamming his meaty palm on the counter in accompaniment to his hearty guffaws. Tina glared at him, but he was bent over double and didn't notice the warning glint in her eyes.

"Silas, dear," she hissed, "your fly is open."

Revenge was never sweeter, and she only wished she had a camera to record Si's face for posterity. He whirled around as fast as a tornado in full spate, and when he looked down at his jeans it set Kathy Sue off again. This got Silas's back up, and he and his nemesis were still vociferously slinging insults at each other as they left the restaurant.

By the time Tina arrived at the ranch the sun was setting in a blaze of glory. She parked her car by the barn so it wouldn't be visible from the drive, and took deep breaths of the clean, cold air as she walked toward the house. The tall ponderosa pines that framed the large A-frame seemed tipped in gold, and the pristine beauty of the landscape suited her mood exactly.

That's the way thinking of Steve made her feel, she realized. Her memories of the past weeks were magical, each one a golden strand spun by fairy fingers. Every time he looked at her she felt beautiful, and her growing confidence in her importance to him had altered her in ways she barely understood. Although he never spoke the words, she was certain he loved her. The knowledge brought her a joy so great that the whole world seemed colored by her happiness.

She had reached the veranda, and after she walked up the steps she dropped her suitcase near the front door. Her other arm was filled with a huge bag of Christmas decorations and gaily wrapped gifts, which she shifted onto her hip as she clumsily searched her purse for the key. With a murmur of triumph she withdrew it, just then noticing that the door was already open a crack. Could Steve have taken an earlier flight and gotten home ahead of schedule? Just the thought of having him so close made her tremble with eagerness.

She stepped into the living room, her eyes immediately seeking the tree. A short man scrambled up from a squatting position, his wide smile showing tobacco-stained teeth with an endearing gap in the middle. "Max?"

His hand was spread over his chest, and he drew in a deep breath. "You about scared the sh—life out of me, Mrs. Taggert."

Her reply was accompanied by a fond smile. "You don't have to clean up your language for me, Max. Believe me, I hear worse on a daily basis. And by the way, I thought we'd gotten around to first names when you helped me with the tree yesterday."

"Steve would have my a—hide tacked to the barn door if I didn't show you proper respect, ma'am."

"Oh, pooh! I promise I'll protect you."

He rubbed the bridge of his nose, his expression reflective. "Begging your pardon, but you've never seen the boss in a temper, Miss Tina."

She supposed "Miss Tina" was better than nothing, and she was anxious to hear more about Steven Michaels's temper. When he stepped forward to relieve her of her bag of goodies, she asked Max, "If he's that ornery, why don't you quit?"

He looked shocked. "Hey, don't get me wrong. When Steve loses his cool there's usually a darn good reason. He's a fine man, and a fair boss. You can't ask for better than that. Why, when my dad died he gave me two months paid leave so I could help my mother with the funeral and everything. I told him I didn't need that much time, but he said he wasn't doing it for me. He said a mother needed her children around her at a time like that."

A lump rose in Tina's throat as she remembered what Steve had told her about the mother he'd never known. Somehow his consideration for Max's mother meant so much more when weighed against the knowledge of his own abandonment. According to Steve that flighty, irresponsible girl had been little more than a child herself, and the realization brought tears of pity to her eyes. How tragic that she would never know what she had given up in her son.

Max's voice penetrated her thoughts. "I've checked out all the lights and extension cords like you asked me to, Miss Tina. Have I strung them up the way you wanted?"

Even unadorned, the tall, wide-branched pine looked wonderful, and she was glad it had been topped and not cut down. Although she loved the symbolism of the holiday season it represented, her conscience wouldn't have let her rest if a tree had been destroyed just to provide them with a few days of pleasure. This way she could enjoy its loveliness, while knowing the living roots were still embedded deeply in the earth.

"It looks wonderful, Max," she said softly. "Thank you so much for all your help."

"It was my pleasure," he replied with an inclination of his head. "I usually go home to Wyoming for the holidays, and I always hate leaving the boss alone in this big house. I've been with him for five years, and in all that time he's never had a tree."

"I know his attitude about Christmas only too well, Max. A few weeks ago he told me it was for kids, and that adults should have more sense." She gestured toward the tree, her expression worried. "I hope he isn't angry with me about this."

Max grinned at her, giving her a thumbs-up sign. "If he hollers, you send him to me and I'll straighten him out," he promised. "He may run the best damn spread in California, but if all us boys walk off the ranch he'll be in sh—very deep trouble."

Her eyes sparkled, and she gave a brief shake of her head. "We'll show him, Max!"

"About time somebody did, and me and the boys are placing our bets on you, ma'am."

After Max departed, Tina raced up the stairs to unpack. She had only brought necessities for tonight and tomorrow, but there was no way the gorgeous negligee and matching peignoir she withdrew from the case could be termed a necessity. Mere wisps of burgundy satin and white lace caressed her fingertips as she held them against her, and her mouth curved into a sensuous smile of anticipation.

After depositing her toiletries in the bathroom, she hung her clothes in the walk-through closet adjoining the dressing area. She studied them, noticing how right they looked next to Steve's. With an impatient shake of her head she glanced at the elegant new watch strapped to her wrist, a twenty-ninth-birthday present from her mother and father.

For a brief moment she closed her eyes, considering how different her life would have been if she had given in to her parents' urgings to join them in Arizona after Dennis died. She would never have met Steve, and that was unimaginable. Also, she would have missed the satisfaction she'd gained from making Deli-Cacy a paying proposition. The last few years had been hard, but she had grown in independence and self-sufficiency. Those were qualities her mom and dad respected, and she knew they were proud of her.

She missed them so much and hoped they could come for a visit soon. Unfortunately, that line of thinking dimmed some of her excitement. Her parents were very traditional in their views, and they wouldn't be pleased to find their daughter living with a man to whom she wasn't married. That was one aspect of moving here she hadn't considered. But she was a grown woman, she told herself staunchly, and she had to live her life in the way that suited her best. With more of an effort than she would have admitted, she shrugged away her disquiet and quickly reentered the bedroom.

The last of the daylight was tracing shadowy patterns across the heavy down comforter on the bed, and with a laugh she raised her eyes to the ceiling overhead. Immediately her heart felt lighter as she recalled that nerve-wracking dinner party, and the sensuous promise in Steve's voice when he offered to show her his skylight.

Her mouth firmed with determination. She would follow his example and take first things first, she vowed silently. There was no use worrying about the future, which usually took care of itself no matter how many plans were made in advance. Anyway, by the time her mom and dad visited she might already be Steve's wife. That thought was a heady one, and as she crossed the open landing she admonished herself for wasting time with all this soul searching.

Another glance at her watch had her uttering a surprised gasp. She couldn't believe how much time had already passed since she'd arrived. If she didn't get a move on, she wasn't going to be prepared for Steve when he got home. Her footsteps were light and impatient as she hurried down the staircase, her hand skimming the curved banister. She tried to keep her thoughts upon practicalities, but the memory of a certain man kept getting in the way. First take care of the tree and then take a relaxing bath, she decided. She was just glad she'd had the foresight to prepare for tonight's meal last evening.

It took her less than an hour to finish decorating the tree, and she stepped back for a moment to admire her handiwork. Although she wanted to linger, she resisted the impulse. She wiped her hands with satisfied thoroughness on the seat of her jeans, her mind on the decadently opulent sunken tub upstairs. She'd brought her favorite lilac-scented bath oils and body powder, and by the time she was finished she was going to smell and feel as seductive as possible. Considering how nervous she was becoming, she needed all the morale boosting she could get.

The Jacuzzi jets eased the muscles that had tensed in anticipation of Steve's arrival, and by the time she returned downstairs she felt relaxed to the point of somnolence. Yawning, she tucked her long gown and matching peignoir over her slippered feet, and curled up against the banked pillows on the couch. She gave another yawn and settled herself more comfortably, her eyes blinking sleepily as she gazed at the twinkling lights of the tree.

* * *

That was the way Steve found her when he stepped in out of the cold, a sleeping beauty waiting for him to come home. For what seemed an eternity he stood just inside the oval archway, his chest tightening with emotion as he studied the scene before him. The tree flickering with dancing lights was like a scene out of a picture postcard. It reminded him so clearly of his boyhood dreams that he had to swallow to ease the ache in his throat.

Then his gaze returned to Christina, and he felt the blood course heatedly through his veins. Dear God in heaven, she was more beautiful than anything he could have imagined. Her softly curling hair was spread around her face, the light from the fire burnishing the red-gold strands trapped inside the soft brown halo.

Unable to take his eyes from her, he shrugged out of his overcoat and sport jacket. Dropping them into a nearby chair, he moved across the room and stopped beside her. If he could have seen his face at that moment he would have been amazed . . . as well as disturbed. The hard lines of his mouth had softened, and his eyes held a yearning for all the things he'd wanted and never had.

Christina awakened and saw the tenderness in his gaze. She blinked her long lashes to dash away the last traces of sleep, and smiled shyly. "Merry Christmas, Steve."

"Merry Christmas, honey."

The words issued from his throat with gravelly huskiness as he looked down at her. There was a pain somewhere deep inside him, making its presence known in poignant echoes from the past. For Steve, Christmas had meant only token offerings, given with little thought and even less care.

He had been the unwanted child standing on the fringes of the family, alone and unable to break into the charmed circle. What he wouldn't have given then for a hug, or merely a warm smile of approval. But none had ever been forthcoming, and the holiday season had only increased his loneliness.

His glance drifted to the tree, and a muscle pulsed in his jaw when he noticed the gaily wrapped packages at its base. "I thought Santa arrived on Christmas Eve?"

He hated the forced jocularity in his voice and mentally berated himself for the foolishness of his behavior. He was out of his element, and damned uncomfortable with the tangible evidence of Christina's generosity.

"Are you angry with him for coming early?"

He heard the question in her voice, asking for reassurance. Abruptly he shook his head, his gaze returning to her pensive features. "Of course not. Why would you think that?"

"Because you have the most ferocious scowl on your face."

His mouth formed a wry smile. "I'm not used to

him coming at all," he admitted softly. "I never celebrate Christmas."

"Then don't you think it's about time you did?"

There was an awkward silence, and he shifted uneasily. He wanted to grab hold of her and thank her for her consideration in the only way he knew how. Yet he thought he might be misinterpreting this whole situation, and was afraid to take anything for granted. He had set the boundaries of their relationship to give her time to be comfortable with him, and he didn't want to blow it now.

"I want to do whatever makes you happy, Christina. I'd like you to feel at home here."

She looked like an earnest little girl as she lay watching his reactions to her planned surprise. "Then you still want me to move in with you, Steve?"

"You know I do."

She sighed in relief and scolded him. "I thought you might be angry to find me here."

His brow slanted mockingly. "Why would I give you a key if I didn't want you to use it?"

"You could have changed your mind."

He gave her a rakish grin, his reply muted and intense as he whispered, "Not a chance, woman."

She pointed to the tree, her face eager once more. "Do you like my surprise?"

He glanced in the direction of her pointing finger, and then away. For all of his adult life he had surrounded himself with the things money could buy. For the first time he realized that's all they were—just inanimate objects with no meaning beyond their monetary value. There had been no Christmas trees, no colored lights or warm rooms filled with a woman waiting to open her arms to him.

"Steve?"

He saw her baffled frown as she tried to interpret the reason for his silence, and hastened to reassure her. "I don't know what to say, honey. No one else has ever done this kind of thing for me, and I guess I'm a bit self-conscious."

"But are you pleased?"

"That doesn't even begin to cover what I'm feeling right now."

It was the truth, he suddenly realized. The gift Christina had just given him was without price, because it came from her heart. As he remembered the selfishness he'd always indulged in, he wanted to tell her he wasn't worthy of her kindness. In his blindness he had counted his coins like a miser, without realizing they were worthless. In his arrogance he had convinced himself he had everything he could ever need or want, without knowing how much he was missing.

He had called this ranch his home, but it had never amounted to more than expensive sections of plaster and glass. There was no heart to an empty house, and it had always been empty. He hadn't had a heart to give, to anything or anyone. The knowledge cut through him, but he knew it was the truth. There was only one thing of permanence a man could count on in his life—himself!

Buildings could burn to the ground, and a woman could walk away. Nothing was forever, and his resolve hardened as the words dispersed the sentimental ramblings of his thoughts. Right now Christina was here, and that was enough for him. At last he would have the kisses and soft smiles for which he had yearned, and he felt his heartbeat quicken at the thought.

Steve knelt beside the couch and placed his hand against a soft, sleep-flushed cheek. "Have I told you yet how beautiful you look?"

"You've been extremely remiss, Mr. Michaels."

"Shall I show my gratitude?"

The brightness of her smile faltered slightly. "I don't want gratitude, Steve."

"Then what do you want?"

Steve was suddenly afraid to hear her answer. *Don't ask for what I can't give you,* his mind cried. He didn't want any meaningless promises between them. With a groan he sought to distract her attention from his question. His mouth brushed across her closed eyelids, the delicate angle of her jaw, the tip of her chin. The diversion worked, and she gave her approval with a soft sigh.

"I'm so glad you're home, Steve. Dinner's ready to pop in the microwave whenever you're ready. Are you hungry?"

"Starving," he replied absently. He couldn't

stop looking at her mouth. "Do I have time for a shower first?"

She laughed and wrinkled her nose teasingly. "I'll make time."

"That bad?"

"That good," she responded lightly.

At the expression in her eyes Steve was overcome with an urgent need to get closer to her, and he bent down and placed his mouth against her smooth forehead. He was barely touching her, and yet the tremor that shook him was shocking in its force. There was a fierceness to the heat spreading throughout his body, and he was disconcerted by the intensity of his desire. He wanted her more than he'd ever wanted anything in his life before, and the realization scared the hell out of him.

Abruptly he rose to his feet, his expression suddenly distant. "I'll head for that shower now. You stay there and rest, and I'll help you with dinner when I come back down."

"All right," she agreed, her voice again sounding uncertain. "I'll be waiting for you."

He walked away on legs that felt stiff and uncoordinated, not even pausing long enough to collect his suitcases from the foyer. Her quiet voice followed him as he climbed the stairs. "I'll be waiting for you." The words were both a promise and a torment. As he entered his bedroom and began stripping off his clothes, he realized he had been waiting for her all of his life.

CHAPTER EIGHT

The fear of losing Christina overwhelmed Steve and brought a frown to his face, but with ruthless determination he pushed it aside. As he stepped into the shower he smelled her scent lingering in the bathroom, and inhaled deeply, as though to make it a part of himself. He was reminded of flowers and golden afternoons, of frisky colts running free in a green pasture, and of sitting beside a clear stream with the sun hot on his back.

In the spring he would take Christina to a secluded spot he knew of along the banks of Bear River, and he would teach her to fish. He could visualize her there vividly, and as he washed himself his mind flowed with the running water. There was so much he wanted to learn about her; so many experiences he wanted to share. She was like a fever in his blood, and he wondered if those were the feelings she thought of as love. If so, the affliction would resolve itself, he thought, his mouth twisting bitterly, his certainty gained by a lifetime of disappointment. Time and association would eventually provide a cure.

But while they were together he would give her anything she could ever need, and when it ended he would provide for her future. She would have no regrets, he promised himself, ignoring his nagging conscience as he rinsed the soap from his body.

Steve felt torn between conflicting desires. Christina was a woman of strong moral character, who had grown up with strict but loving parents. In their world a physical relationship meant marriage, commitment, and family. In one way he would be committed, because for him there would be no other women while they were together. But that was all he could offer her, he thought, unable to see any other way for them. It was a lot easier to end a live-in relationship than a marriage, especially if children were involved.

At the thought of his child growing inside Christina's body his mouth went dry and his throat tightened with emotion. Then he caught himself, realizing that he had no right to indulge such imaginings. He wouldn't deliberately tie her to him with that kind of an obligation.

Steve thought of all the things he could do for her to make her life easier, and his rigidly compressed mouth eased into a smile. She was stubbornly independent, but she would soon realize she didn't have to rely only upon herself. He would give anything to keep her by his side, and never count the cost. God, how he hated to watch her killing herself running that damn catering service! Soon there would be no need for any of that, he assured himself, not once she belonged to him.

He shut off the shower, his body leaping in anticipation at the thought of them together. She, too, would give him everything he could ever want from a woman. She was gentle and kind, and had a generosity toward those she cared about that never ceased to amaze him. She would give herself completely, without reservation, and he would delight in teaching her to appreciate the sensuality of her nature. He felt his body stir; just the idea of her hands and mouth on him made him tremble with desire.

Christina was busy at the kitchen sink when he went in search of her, and with a stealthy tread he crept up behind her. His hands spanned her waist, and he pulled her back to rest against his hard body. "I missed you, honey."

She leaned her head against him and breathed appreciatively. "You smell delicious."

"Is that all you have to say?" he asked, wriggling his fingers against her waist.

"Steve!" With a giggle she squirmed to evade his tickling hands.

"Well?" he asked warningly.

She raised a hand and caressed his jawline. "Mmmm, you shaved off your bristles."

Abruptly he whirled her around in his arms and began nibbling at her earlobe. As an interrogation

135

tactic this did the trick, and with a sigh of surrender Tina wound her arms around his neck. "I missed you too."

His warm mouth slid to her throat, and he felt his nerve ends tingle when she gasped in response. In a voice he barely recognized as his own, he asked, "Are you going to show me how much?"

Her own voice trembled betrayingly. "Do you still want me to?"

Steve had never believed in fairy tales, yet as he held this woman in his arms he wanted to believe. Dear God, he wanted to believe so badly she would always care for him. But life had taught him reality, and even as he pressed her closer he knew it was too late for pretense. He'd long ago lost his innocent faith in love. He wasn't the kind of person who inspired that tender emotion, and so for him it was just another word; a romantic fantasy which occurred in the imagination. Only a fool would place his trust in something that didn't exist.

He shook off his momentary depression and brushed the sweet curve of her cheek with his mouth. "Can't you feel how much I want you?"

Tina groaned as he deliberately rocked his hips against the cradle of her thighs, and she arched her back with a mewling little cry. He smiled his satisfaction against her throat, and his breath came faster. Christina was a woman whose earthy needs matched his own. He had sensed that in her from the beginning, and the reassurance increased his

136

desire for her until he felt as though he were going to burst apart. Oh, yes, they would both gain a great deal from their relationship, however temporary it proved to be. The admission echoed hollowly in his mind.

Then he pulled back to look at her, and the guilt that swept over him left him feeling like the selfish bastard he knew he was. Her eyes were slumbrous with passion, and yet they held an intensity of feeling he didn't want to acknowledge. He saw her gentle spirit reflected in her smile, and knew he would destroy that innocent trust if he didn't leave her alone.

He might be confident of his ability to satisfy her on a physical level, but for a woman like Christina that would never be enough. Emotionally he could never give her what she needed, and his insides twisted in pain and panic. She deserved so much more than he could offer her, he thought. She was a dreamer, and he was a man without dreams. They were too far apart in outlook and ideals, and he should end it now before she was hurt.

But even as that thought entered his mind he was lowering his head, his mouth hungry and mobile as it slanted over hers. Her warmth and sweetness pierced the cold of his isolation, and everything became clear to him in that instant. He couldn't let her go . . . not yet! Eventually she would be the one to leave him, but until then he would accept whatever she was willing to give him. He would grasp at the peace she offered his soul, and prepare himself for the time he would once again be alone.

With breathless reluctance Tina pushed against his chest. "What's wrong, Steve?"

Steve marveled at her perception where he was concerned, and was determined to erase the worried look in her eyes. He wanted her to know only happiness with him, not fear or pain or concern. "I'm fine, honey. It was a boring flight, and I guess I'm a little tired."

She tilted her head, some of the tension leaving her body as she teased, "Didn't you flirt with the stewardess to pass the time?"

"No, she just sat on my lap to chat awhile."

She jabbed a well-aimed fist in his ribs. "Do you want to keep breathing, Michaels?"

Since he was trying to recover from her punch to his solar plexis, the question was amazingly apt. "Does the condemned man get a last meal?"

His brown eyes held such a winsome appeal that she laughed and patted him on the stomach. "Are you very hungry?"

At the touch of her hand he inhaled sharply, and leaned forward to trace the soft curve of her mouth with his tongue. "I'm hungry for you," he murmured. "Are you hungry, too, Christina?"

She pulled back and gave him a prim look from beneath her lashes. "For chicken casserole."

He kissed the tip of her nose. "Spoilsport."

His eyes followed her as she moved around the kitchen, his attention more on the way her negligee

138

clung to the curves of her body than on the lettuce he was shredding into a wooden bowl. "You make it very difficult to concentrate dressed like that."

She glanced over her shoulder, her expression warmly provocative. "It takes concentration to fix a salad?"

He gave her question serious consideration, then ruined the effect with an expressive leer. "If you'll notice, I'm getting more lettuce on the counter than in the bowl."

They worked together companionably for a time, and Steve experienced a contentment he'd never known before. The frustration and loneliness of this last week without Tina was eased by her presence, and he wondered at her ability to both soothe and excite him. He enjoyed the swishing sound of satin as she moved about the room, and yet he ached to strip the gown from her body. He savored the sound of her voice humming a soft melody, and yet he wanted to muffle the tune with his mouth.

"Are you ready?"

His head swiveled to look at her, a myriad of delicious visions aroused by her innocent question. He could visualize a tangle of arms and legs, and two passionate bodies writhing in ecstasy. Oh, yes! He was more than ready for her, he thought yearningly. He was ready to carry her upstairs to his bed, to kiss every inch of skin he uncovered, and to die a little death in her arms. He was so ready he was about to lose his mind.

"Steve?"

At the sound of his name he stared down at the bowl he held in his hands, and grinned ruefully. "I'm really not a bad cook, but you'd never guess that by my performance tonight."

"You like to cook?"

His grin widened at her obvious surprise. "Yeah," he admitted sheepishly, "unless I'm dead on my feet."

She cocked her head and stared at him with dancing eyes. "Are you dead on your feet tonight?"

He growled with mock ferocity and started toward her. "Just let me get my hands on you, and I'll show you I'm very alive when I'm off my feet, woman!"

She sprang toward the dining room, her laughter floating behind her. "Bring in the salad, caveman."

The paneled dining room was arranged with red linen napkins and candles, the festive arrangement set off by the snow-white cloth draped over the table. It was an heirloom Tina had brought with her, crocheted by her great-great-grandmother. Seeing something of her own gracing Steve's furniture now seemed so right, she thought, finally realizing that this would soon be her home.

Dinner was pleasant and leisurely, punctuated by conversation and comfortable silences. Steve told her about the stallion he'd bought at the auction, his face enthusiastic as he recounted the animal's fine points. Tina then described her week, which had been busy but deadly dull.

Propping her elbow on the table beside her empty plate, she rested her chin on her open palms. "Without you around to fight with," she admitted with her usual candor, "it hardly seemed worth getting out of bed in the morning."

"After tonight we won't have frustration as an excuse," he teased. "What are we going to fight about from now on?"

She shrugged with a nonchalance she hoped was convincing. "We'll find something else to stave off boredom."

"I can think of a few things I've got planned."

She flushed at the look in his eyes and jumped to her feet to begin stacking the dishes. "I'll just bet you can!"

He stood up to help her clear the table, but as she moved to pass him he leaned forward and whispered, "There's only one problem, Christina."

She hesitated just a second too long, caught by the wicked glint in his eyes. Although she knew it wasn't prudent to ask, she couldn't resist satisfying her curiosity. "What is it?"

"You're still not going to want to get up in the morning."

Trying to subdue the heat creeping up her neck, she made a rude face. "All talk and no action, big man."

"That's twice you've thrown down the gauntlet," he warned with a rakish grin. "I hope you know what you're doing."

With a poise she envied he followed her into the kitchen and opened the door of the dishwasher. "You rinse and I'll load."

"You're a bossy devil, Mr. Michaels."

He cast her a sidelong glance through half-closed lids, and grinned. "Two pairs of hands can work twice as fast, and I'm in a hurry, Christina."

Since she had a very good idea of why he was in such a rush, she didn't dare question him any further. From the corner of her eye she saw him smile knowingly, and she kept her attention glued to the sink. There was a good reason for the sudden attack of nerves she was experiencing, but understanding didn't solve the problem. What she wouldn't give to be able to make some witty rejoinder, she acknowledged wretchedly. But in a verbal skirmish she always came out the loser, and the maddening man at her side loved watching her lose her composure.

Soon the kitchen was restored to order, and they carried their coffee into the den. While Steve lit a fire, she studied her surroundings with a contemplative air. "This is my favorite room in the house," she admitted.

Brushing fine-grained woodchips from his hands, Steve got to his feet and stretched out beside her on the couch. As he reached for his coffee, he asked, "What do you like most about it?"

She took a sip from the mug in her hand, her

brow wrinkled in thought. "The colors, I guess. Cream and brown and apricot are all such warm, comfortable shades. But I think what I really like is its shape," she said after a slight pause. "What gave you the idea of an octagon room, Steve?"

He shrugged, but she could tell he was pleased by her question. "I wanted something unique," he said. "A place with lots of windows where I wouldn't feel closed in."

She nodded her understanding and finished the last of her drink. Placing it on the serving cart, she tucked her slippered feet beneath her and sat back with a sigh. The heat from the fire bathed her face with warmth, and she turned to him with a contented smile. "The open fire is nice," she said. "Although I'm surprised you don't have wood stoves for heating the house."

"I can afford my electrical bill, and like you I enjoy an open fire."

She was running out of topics of conversation, and she could tell by his expression that he was enjoying her dilemma. But chattering passed the time and kept her mind off that damn skylight over his bed. With assumed brightness she asked, "Why don't you have a housekeeper?"

"Someone comes in twice a week to do the heavy cleaning, but I've never liked the idea of a woman dogging my footsteps. I've always taken care of myself, and I figure it's a little late for me to change my bachelor ways."

The instant he saw her reaction to his admission, he wanted to cut his throat. With a terse expletive he reached out to her, his concerned gaze taking in her sudden pallor. "I didn't mean that the way it sounded, Christina."

But she twisted to avoid his seeking hand, her eyes meeting his with determination in their depths. "You're really not sure about this, are you, Steve?"

He didn't pretend to misunderstand her. "I know I want you with me, Christina."

"For a convenient sex partner?"

Her voice cut into him with razor sharpness, but there had to be honesty between them. With another woman he might have whispered reassuring lies they both knew were false, but Christina didn't play those kinds of games. She wasn't the kind of person to accept insincere platitudes, and he respected her too much to offer them to her.

"You know that isn't all there is," he said defensively. "But I'm not going to deny that I want you in my bed."

Thick lashes shielded the expression in her eyes. "Just what do you feel for me, Steve?"

The bluntness of her inquiry robbed him of breath, and he paused before saying carefully, "I . . . care for you."

"I hear a 'but' in there somewhere," she said, her mouth tightening around the words.

"But I don't want all the ties that bind," he admitted harshly.

She winced at his honesty and then gave a rueful

laugh that held no humor. "Then sex will be the most important part of our relationship," she remarked dully. "What happens when the earth stops shaking, Steve?"

"That will depend on you."

She looked at him in surprise and shivered at the remoteness of his expression. He saw the betraying movement and ran his hand across the back of his neck. Rubbing the tense muscles he found there, he raised his head to gauge her reaction to what he was going to say.

"I'm not the kind of man who can promise you forever, but I think you already know that. Don't you?"

She nodded and studied the hands she'd clasped in front of her. "Are you promising me anything, Steve?"

Slowly he drew her to his side, his breathing heavy with suppressed anxiety. He was bleeding inside at the thought of losing her now, but she had to make a choice with everything out in the open. He placed his hands on her shoulders, and his fingers tightened nervously.

"I'll be a gentle lover, and I'll do my best to make you happy, Christina," he said quietly. "Those are the only promises I can give. Will they be enough for you?"

He felt her stiffen, and he knew whatever decision she made would be final and irrevocable. The urge to use the sexual tension vibrating between them was strong, and yet he didn't want to seduce her into giving him the answer he wanted. As he waited, the minutes seemed to stretch into hours, and he wondered where he found the strength to withstand this subtle torment.

Steve felt smothered by the silence stretching tautly between them. But then she straightened and deliberately met his dark, haunted eyes. Her features reflected both sadness and certainty as she whispered, "They will have to be."

He drew in a relieved breath and felt her arms go around his waist as he pulled her close. "You won't be sorry you stayed with me."

His arms tightened convulsively, and the forehead she pressed against his chest moved in a negative gesture. "No promises, remember?"

"No promises," he repeated heavily.

Tina had made her decision, but only she knew how much it had cost her in pride and self-respect. To know there was love on only one side didn't make for an ideal situation, but it was all he could offer her. She loved him enough for both of them, and the alternative to becoming his mistress wasn't one she cared to contemplate. She tried to convince herself she didn't need a rose garden to be happy, but the hands she slipped around his neck were fiercely possessive.

Steve lifted her in his arms, and she clung to him with all the strength in her body. As he carried her out of the den and across the hall, she felt his warmth easing the ache of misery in her chest. When he began to climb the stairs to his bedroom, she inhaled his masculine scent and surrendered to the inevitability of the moment.

This was what she wanted, she thought bracingly, just one perfect rose to mature inside her heart. And if the flower of her love had sharp, piercing thorns, then she would bear the pain willingly. Each moment together would add another petal to the fragile bloom, and maybe someday Steve would be unable to resist its beauty. *In the spring,* her heart whispered. Maybe her love would take root and blossom inside of him in the spring.

By the time they reached their destination, the trembling that had begun in her fingers had spread tentacles of anticipation throughout her body. The room was silvered with the moonglow that filtered down from the skylight overhead, and as she stood with Steve beside the large bed, its radiance softened the harsh contours of his face.

With wondering eyes she looked up at him. "You're so beautiful," she whispered.

He seemed disconcerted for a moment, and then he smiled. "You're the one who is beautiful, Christina."

She found no reassurance in his remark, and when he began to slide the peignoir from her shoulders she became rigid with distress.

His hands stilled abruptly, and there was an expression of dread darkening his eyes. "Have you changed your mind?"

She stared at the middle button on his shirt and shook her head.

"Then what's wrong, honey?"

She muttered something he couldn't hear, and he tilted her chin until he could watch the movement of her mouth. "Now try again," he demanded encouragingly.

Her chest rose as she drew in a deep breath. "I—I'm feeling absurdly self-conscious, Steve. After the last time when I . . . when you . . ."

"When I humiliated you?"

His voice was laced with self-contempt, and she closed her eyes on a wave of misery. "I know I'm being silly."

His hands slid up her shoulders until they rested against her warm cheeks. "It's my fault you feel uneasy," he admitted remorsefully. "I behaved like an idiot that night."

That brought a smile, albeit a strained one, to her face. "You weren't exactly diplomatic."

"Maybe this will help," he murmured.

Rapidly he began to unbutton his shirt, and while she watched the rest of his clothing followed. Tina's eyes grew round as the superb dimensions of his body were revealed, and this time when he moved to undress her she made no protest. Burgundy satin slid from her skin with a whisper of sound, forming a lustrous mound at her feet.

"Now we're vulnerable to each other, Christina."

She nodded and stepped into his arms. "I love you, Steve."

He started to speak, but she pressed her fingers

to his lips with a smile of understanding. "I know what you're going to say, but please don't. I—I need to be able to tell you, Steve. I need to be able to love you with words as well as my body."

He remained still and silent while her breath whispered the words in gusts of warmth against his flesh, and inwardly she was crying out for him to follow her lead. Tenderly her tongue slipped out to tease a hard nipple through the soft fur covering his chest, and it was as though she had lighted a fuse inside of him.

With stumbling haste he laid her flat on her back upon the cool sheets, his heat and warmth covering her.

"Dear God!" he muttered hoarsely. He tangled his hands in her hair and forced her face up to his. "If it's words you need, I'll give them to you."

Then it began, a seduction by voice and touch that had her twisting in a ritual dance of pleasure.

A hot, moist tongue bathed a pinkly swollen nipple. "Now you know what you made me feel a moment ago," he groaned.

A roving hand slid across her soft stomach and slipped downward, his fingers finding the goal he was seeking. Deeply they plunged, and when she cried out he whispered, "I can feel your body pulsing against my hand, stretching and growing damp to ease my path. I want to be inside you, honey."

She moaned with equal fervor, her hips matching the rhythm of his hand until she grew taut with the agony of wanting. His suckling mouth at her breast followed their lead, and she sobbed with a need so great, she thought she would faint before she reached the peak her body was reaching toward. But then it was there, and she lunged toward his tormenting hand until she shuddered with satiation.

"You make me burn, Christina."

He moved over her, bracing his weight on his arms as he crooned, "So sweet. So soft and sweet and hot."

"Steve," she cried, once again caught up in the magic of his touch. "Oh, please, I . . ."

His eyes glittered down at her in the darkness. "Take me into you, sweetness."

In a mindless frenzy she complied, his hard fullness easing the ache that was building once again. Their movements blended as though they were made for each other, their passion peaking beneath the benevolent glow of moonlight.

Strong hands grasped her hips, raising her until she accepted even more of him. "Christina," he cried, his head thrown back in an agony of sensation. "Oh, honey, love me . . . love me!"

She felt as though she were being torn apart by the quaking shudders that rippled through her, until at last Steve found his own completion with the taste of her name on his lips. Then he slumped against her, his vulnerability total as he lay in satiated weakness.

Christina held him, loving him with every breath she drew. In the throes of passion he had pleaded with her to love him, and although the cry had been dredged from his subconscious, she was content. She had given and would continue to give, because his needs were more important to her than her own.

Tina realized that she had discovered a new truth. In his arms they had merged together into a whole, and for that brief moment they had been completely dependent on each other. That was love, she realized, a sharing of strength and weakness, pleasure and pain. There had been no promises spoken, and yet the simple existence of love, whether reciprocated or not, was a promise in itself. Tina found contentment in the fact that she belonged to Steve in the most basic way possible, because that was the way she wanted it to be. She could face the future with confidence, because tonight a new Christina had burst forth from the ashes of the old.

CHAPTER NINE

"Steven, what are you doing?"

The question was asked lazily, Tina's drowsy eyes lowered as she watched the end of her fishing line being tugged downstream by the rushing silver, foam-flecked waters of Bear River. She gave a contented sigh and squirmed into a more comfortable position against Steven's broad chest. Her elbows were propped against his drawn-up thighs, and as she shifted her weight they dug into him.

"Ouch! Don't you know better than to distract a man when he's fishing, woman?"

"Is that what you call it?"

Her body shook with the force of his silent laughter. "I'm just showing you the correct way to hold the rod."

She sniffed disparagingly. "The rod is not attached to my chest, Mr. Michaels."

"It isn't?"

"No!"

This time his laughter was given full expression, and she heard as well as felt the deep bass rumble.

"If you keep jabbing me with it, it will be. Don't grip it so tightly, honey. It's not going to run away."

"And if your hands slip again," she warned, a secret smile curving her lips, "I'm going to smack them."

"I'm shaking in my boots."

"You'll be doubled over," she threatened sweetly, "if I dig my elbow into another portion of your anatomy."

"I think it's hard enough to take it."

She swallowed a laugh and began choking instead. When she managed to get her breath back she hissed, "You're incorrigible!"

"You were the one who didn't want to put waders on and learn how to fish properly," he reminded her with feigned innocence. "This is what you get for being such a sissy."

"I wasn't being a sissy," she snapped indignantly. "I had a very good reason for preferring to fish from shore."

"What was it?"

"You said you were going to hold me so I wouldn't be swept downstream."

"So what's the difference?" He nuzzled the back of her sun-warmed hair with his mouth. "I'm holding you now."

"The difference is wet."

"I would have looked out for you."

"Hah! With my luck you would have gotten distracted and dropped us both in the drink," she retorted. "We're having a warm spring, but I didn't fancy a swim. In case you don't know, this river is swollen because of melting snow in the Sierras."

"That isn't all that's swollen." He groaned.

She tried to sound outraged but spoiled the effect with a giggle. "You need your mouth washed out with soap, you letch."

With a derisive snort Steve allowed his hands to slip a little farther into the opening of the long-sleeved cotton shirt she wore. It was one of his, and it gave him immense pleasure to see her wearing it. When she had put it on this morning over a pair of tight, faded jeans, he had grinned at her like an enamored idiot.

With the sleeves rolled up to her elbows and her ponytail swinging, she'd looked like a rustic Lolita. His grin widened as his mouth began pulling at the wisps of hair curling against the back of her neck. She had protested vociferously when he dragged her back upstairs, he remembered, but by the time he'd tugged her jeans off she had stopped arguing.

"Steven, I think I've caught something," Tina squealed, sitting up straight with more energy than grace.

He wiped his tongue over the sore lip he'd just dug his teeth into, and muttered, "Your line is probably snagged on a rock."

She shook her head, and her ponytail slapped him across the face. "It's a fish, I know it is!"

He whipped his head back, his cheek stinging. "It's too late in the day for them to be biting."

Her disappointment was obvious. "Are you sure?"

"Uh-huh." His calloused fingers abandoned her neckline and began to wander in the vicinity of her waist. "Now, why don't you lean back against me again and relax?"

"I can't relax when you're doing that," she said in exasperation. "And in case you've forgotten, it's not my fault we got a late start this morning."

Not quite trusting his expertise as a fisherman, she began to wind the reel with stubborn persistence. "If it's too late for the fish to be biting, then what are we doing here?"

"Enjoying the scenery?" he asked, his husky voice betraying his real motive.

His entire concentration was focused on easing his shirt over her hips. Once his task was accomplished, his hands were free to climb steadily up her rib cage. She turned her head to glare at him in suspicion. "Your hands are slipping again."

The appendages in question had reached two pouting nipples, and she gasped when he began rolling them between his forefingers and thumbs. "Have I ever told you what pretty breasts you have?"

"I think you've mentioned it once or twice."

"Well, you do," he stated, his chest rising and falling in accompaniment to his rapidly thudding heart. "They have to be the prettiest breasts in the world, and they feel so soft and firm when I touch them."

Again her ponytail swiped him, this time across his nose. "Now I know why you didn't want me to put my bra on this morning."

"I just wanted you to be comfortable." His protest was punctuated by a loud sneeze. "That's the gratitude a man gets when he tries to be helpful."

"You sound just like Si."

He chuckled. "Kathy Sue sure enjoys shoving her feminist viewpoints down the poor guy's throat."

She gave him a furious glare. "I notice she's as sweet as pie when you're around. It's sickening the way that woman fawns over you."

"She knows I'm no chauvinist."

"Then she's got a few bats in her belfry," she grunted, the heat of his exploring hands making her dizzy.

He gave a low moan and tightened his thighs around her wriggling hips. "Are you questioning my sterling qualities?"

"If you're no chauvinist, they why did you spend two weeks sulking when I refused to discontinue our catering service?" she asked him in remembered ire.

"I wanted to take care of you."

"I don't need to be taken care of."

There was irony in his voice, as well as a trace of discontent. "That I've discovered to my cost."

She nodded complacently and rubbed the top of

her head against his chin. "For a male chauvinist pig, you're coming along very nicely, darling."

"You mean I'm like putty in your hands," he mumbled in self-disgust. "And I may be a male pig, but I'm no chauvinist, Christina."

"Is that why you threw a hissy fit when I refused to let you buy me a car, or when I insisted on contributing to the household budget?"

The tips of his fingers began to rub lightly across her nipples, a maneuver he knew would distract her. "I was just being logical," he whispered raggedly. "I don't want your help with the groceries, and I like giving you things."

"I refuse to be a kept woman, Steven!"

"You need a car, Christina. That van sucks up gas like it's going out of style," he argued with annoying reason. "On the rare occasions you let Kathy Sue take over a catering job, which isn't often enough to suit me, you have to borrow her car to get home."

"I need a lot of things, but I'll provide them for myself, Steve."

"I can think of one thing you can't provide for yourself," he muttered hotly.

She could too. His hands set up a circular motion against her sensitive flesh, and her breathing pattern was beginning to match his in rapidity. At the same time she noticed that her reeling efforts were definitely slowing down. Languidly, she tilted her head to the side so his warm mouth had easier access to her neck. "Steven?"

"Mmmm?"

"If that isn't a fish, what is it?"

He squinted over her shoulder. "Well, I'll be damned!"

She smiled smugly and shot him a provocative glance. "I told you."

"That's enough out of you, Miss Smarty Pants."

A giggle bubbled up and was borne away by the breeze. "At least you let me put those back on this morning."

With Steve's help she landed her catch, then eyed the gaping, quivering trout guiltily. "The poor little thing."

"It is not little," he corrected with relish, using a pair of pliers to remove the hook. "This stout sucker is going to taste mighty nice tonight."

Tina saw two bulging eyes watching her and was certain they were pleading for help. She swallowed and turned a little green. "I'm not cooking it!"

He glanced up in surprise, his expression puzzled. "Why not, for heaven's sake?"

"I'd feel like a cannibal."

"I thought you liked fried trout."

"I like the kind you get in the butcher section at the supermarket," she muttered, averting her gaze from the gasping victim of her crime.

He grunted, finally managing to extract the hook. "Once I've gutted it you won't be able to tell the difference."

At the word gutted her sickly pallor intensified.

"Even fried I'll still be able to see it looking at me."

"I'll cut off the head," he replied cheerfully.

"That's gross!"

"There's nothing gross about a dead fish, Christina. They don't even bleed much."

She crossed her arms in front of her and assumed a militant stance. "You're not the one who murdered it!"

"And you will never make a fisherman with that attitude."

He had a point there, and she hated to disappoint him. Studying the scuffed toe of her tennis shoe with great concentration, she said, "That's true, and I'm just being silly."

Since the declaration was accompanied by a mournful sigh, Steve eyed her suspiciously. She was right, he thought in disgust. Even with her head down he could see a betraying shimmer in those lovely green eyes. Then he turned his attention to the still flapping fish, and decided he wanted chicken for dinner after all. At least he wouldn't be the one to feel quilty for wringing its neck!

"Christina?"

She lifted her eyes warily at the sound of her name, and saw Steve meticulously washing his hands in the river. "Did you put the fish in the cooler?" she asked with uncharacteristic timidity.

"No."

She gazed at him with a glimmer of hope in her wide green eyes. "Then where is it?"

He wiped his damp hands against his shirt, his mouth mocking his altruistic impulse. "The damn thing's probably already looking for another way to commit suicide."

"You let it go?" she questioned softly. "You did that for me?"

"Don't think my motives were completely unselfish, Christina." His eyes gleamed wickedly as he rose and began to walk toward her. "I've worked up a hunger for more than fish this afternoon."

Her mouth rounded, and she began slowly backing toward the trees lining the bank. She clutched at her throat and asked, "What if somebody comes?"

He gave her a well-executed leer. "I plan to."

"Steven Michaels, now you're really being gross."

He spread out his open palms for her inspection, but kept moving. "My hands are empty and my conscience is clear."

"It won't be clear if we get arrested."

"Come on, sweetness," he said, his voice rife with sensuality. "You know you want to."

"Steve?"

He placed his arm around her waist and hauled her up the bank and into the thick covering of the woods. "What, my softhearted darling?"

They entered a small clearing. The forest about

them was fragrant and welcoming, but Tina looked nervously around their sylvan glade. "You know that new nightie you bought me last month?"

He began unbuttoning his shirt, and spread it on the soft, moss-covered ground before he seated himself. Then he grinned and pulled her down beside him. "You mean the one you said was indecent?"

"Well, it is," she insisted, pushing at his bare chest when he settled himself on top of her. "The thing's completely transparent, except in a few . . . ahhh . . . strategic places."

"What about it?"

"Why don't we go home so I can model it for you?"

His hands had been busy slipping buttons from their holes, but at her question his eyes lifted to her face. "Now?" he asked huskily.

It took a lot of effort for Tina to stop a triumphant smile from widening her mouth, but she managed to keep her features composed long enough to reply. "Right now," she said, a sultry promise in her whispered tones.

But her triumph was short lived—he grinned and shook his head. "No way, baby!"

With a last flick of his fingers he had the shirt open and her breasts exposed to his hungry gaze. She moaned when his hand reached out to test the weight of one firm, pink-tipped mound. "You're taking unfair advantage, Steven."

"And you love it!"

"I love you, but that's beside the point."

"This point?" he asked, pressing his thumb against a pebble-hard nipple, "or this one?"

His other hand came into play as he spoke, and she clutched his shoulders to stop the earth from shaking.

"I've changed my mind." She groaned, sliding her hands into his hair and pulling his mouth closer to her aching breasts.

"I knew you would."

She heard the trace of smugness in his voice, and her retaliation was swift. "I mean you're not a dirty old man," she muttered defensively.

She shivered when his laugh bathed her puckering nipple, which was now damp from his laving tongue. "I'm not?"

By this time Tina's mental abilities were not at their best, but she managed to remember what she wanted to tell him. "You are—" she moaned when a strong hand unfastened the snap on her jeans and slid inside the opening "—a dirty old fisherman," she finished on a gasp.

Steve tugged off her shoes and started on her jeans. "And you're the prettiest little minnow I've ever caught."

His parted lips began trailing from ankle to thigh, and her breath grew ragged. "Three times in one day can't be good for you, Steve."

"It's good." He sighed, his fingers gently spreading the soft down covering her femininity. "It's so damn good I can hardly stand it."

He was lowering his head to nibble at the treasure he'd uncovered, when an inconsistency in her words finally got through to him. With extreme hopefulness he asked, "Three times?"

She stretched with sensual indolence and laughed gently. "Once this morning, once now, and once tonight when I model that decadent piece of cloth for you."

Reassured by her mathematical ability, Steve didn't bother to respond with anything more than a pleased growl. He was too busy tasting the fruits of his labor, his tongue sliding against her with mind-boggling precision. He was totally enraptured by her scent and taste, his appetite for her voracious.

Christina arched her hips, her hands tangling in his hair. "Oh, Steve, it's . . ."

His tongue wandered over her rippling stomach and paused to relish her breasts while his fingers completed the task his mouth had begun. "It's what?" he questioned, in a voice roughened by arousal.

She waited to give him his answer, too busy fumbling with his zipper to be able to form one single sentence in her mind. But then he was free to come to her, and she felt the heat of him fill her to bursting. "Heaven, darling," she cried. "It's heaven when you make love to me!"

Tina lay limply in a pair of strong arms, staring up at the leafy canopy above them. The sun of late afternoon slipped through the branches in ghostly paths, bathing the two people they sheltered with warmth and light. From the even pattern of his breathing she thought Steve was asleep, until he raised himself up on his elbow to look down at her.

His other hand cupped a breast, while his thumb brushed back and forth against the immediately responsive peak. He smiled with masculine appreciation, a smile that reached his eyes and made them glow like amber gems. "I love going fishing with you, Christina. It's fun!"

He roared with laughter as a healthy blush colored her cheeks.

They took a shower together as soon as they arrived home, both too tired to do more than soap and rinse. Then she started dinner while Steve sorted out his fishing gear, and by the time the meal was finished and they had eaten, Tina's energy level had risen to a new high. Since the evenings were still a little chilly, coffee and hot apple pie were devoured sitting cross-legged before the fireplace in the den. They talked contentedly while finishing dessert, their conversation punctuated with laughter.

When she rose reluctantly to return the used dishes to the kitchen, Steve stopped her with a meaningful smile and laid a caressing hand on her arm. "Aren't you forgetting something?"

She frowned in perplexity, and then her brow cleared. "You want another cup of coffee?"

He shook his head. "Nope."

"Tomorrow is garbage pickup, and we have to carry the cans to the end of the drive?"

"Wrong day," he remarked complacently.

If her hands hadn't been full of cutlery, they would have landed firmly on her hips. "Then what's the matter?" she asked in exasperation. "Have I forgotten to salaam and beg the master's permission to withdraw?"

"Now, that last suggestion has merit."

She grinned. "Up your nose with a rubber hose, O exalted lord."

His laughter was warmly appreciative as he leaned back on his elbow. "Didn't you mention something about modeling for me tonight?"

Her mouth opened, but before she could get a word out he reminded her of her promise. "But I was being coerced," she pointed out.

"A promise is a promise."

She laughed when his eyebrows wriggled. "Are you rotten enough to hold me to words spoken in a moment of extreme mental aberration?" she asked.

"To the core," he replied with certainty.

Her attitude was resigned as she turned to head for the kitchen, but her heart was beating faster than her feet could move. She left the dishes in the sink to soak and hurried upstairs with a distinct sparkle in her eyes. So, he wanted her to model for him, did he? The poor man didn't know what he was in for, she decided without the slightest remorse. She was going to model him right out of his ever-loving gourd!

But when Tina caught sight of her reflection in the dressing room mirror a few minutes later, a great deal, if not all, of her bravado disappeared. The goose bumps that popped out all over her body gave her more covering than the scanty teddy, and she swallowed uneasily. She could not go downstairs in this thing, she thought. *Indecent* wasn't the word to describe see-through black net inset with three minuscule dots of black lace. *Decadent* was more suitable!

The sound of the phone ringing from the bedroom extension made her jump and moisten her dry lips with the tip of her tongue. When the clamor ceased, she knew Steve had answered the summons. Thank heaven for small favors, she thought, wanting to laugh but knowing she'd probably slip into hysteria. Anyway, if she wasn't mistaken, her vocal chords had atrophied.

With unusual clumsiness she began to run a brush through her hair, trying hard not to glance below her neck. The familiar rhythm was soothing, so when Steve's voice called to her from the bedroom she managed not to expire on the spot. Hesitantly she returned her brush to the counter, and sauntered out to meet him with every evidence of composure.

"What is it, dar—?"

The endearment stuck in her throat when she caught sight of the grim-faced man standing beside the bed. A sense of dread kept her motionless. "Steve, what's wrong?"

"Put something on and we'll talk, Christina."

She flinched as though she'd been struck, and hurriedly backed into the dressing room to search for a robe long enough to cover her from neck to ankle. Her hands shook as she sorted through the hangers, and her pale features reflected shocked dismay. She didn't know what had caused the change in Steve, but somehow it concerned her. For some reason he was furious, and she shivered when she remembered the way his cold, expressionless eyes had watched her.

Taking a deep breath, she returned to the bedroom. Steve hadn't moved, and when she hesitated he motioned her toward a chair. "This may take a little while," he informed her dryly.

Biting down on her lower lip, she seated herself without protesting his high-handed behavior. There wasn't much to argue about, she decided wryly, because she doubted if her legs were going to hold her up for very much longer.

Once her gaze returned to his face, she asked, "Why are you angry?"

"Angry doesn't begin to cover what I'm feeling, Christina."

Her fingers began to brush over the soft velour

fabric covering her lap. "I don't understand what's happened, Steve."

"That was your mother on the phone."

The blunt information was given with little inflection, and yet it lashed out at her with stunning force. "My mother? But she wasn't supposed to—"

"No, she wasn't supposed to call here, was she?" he retorted, a sneer destroying the handsome curve of his mouth. "You've always called her."

She flushed guiltily. "Well, yes, but—"

"Your parents don't know you've moved in with me, do they?"

"No," she said faintly. "When I gave them my new address and phone number I mentioned meeting you, and they were both so happy for me I couldn't tell them the truth."

"You were ashamed to tell them we were living together!"

His terse accusation left her speechless, and he finally broke the silence by inquiring, "How long did you think you could continue the deception?"

"I don't know." She shook her head and shrugged. "I didn't see any point in worrying them unnecessarily."

"Unnecessarily?" He shouted the question and raked his hair back with tense fingers. "You felt it unnecessary to explain our relationship to your parents?"

"You don't understand!"

"Try me," he responded sarcastically.

"They have old-fashioned values, Steve," she said hesitantly. "They wouldn't approve of me being here with you."

He looked disgusted. "You sound like a little girl afraid of a spanking."

She leaned her elbow against the arm of the chair and braced her head against her hand. "It isn't that," she responded tiredly. "I'm their only child, and they've always been so proud of me, Steve. I—I couldn't bear to disappoint them."

"No," he said through gritted teeth, "you'd rather lie by omission."

Tina could imagine the shock and embarrassment her mother must have suffered when Steve answered the phone, and closed her eyes on a wave of misery. Helen Carlson was shy and unworldly, and because of her daughter's cowardess she had been subjected to a confrontation for which she was ill prepared.

"It hardly matters now," she responded dully.

Steve's voice was abrasive as he replied, "Don't worry, I covered for you, Christina. The poor woman was so disconcerted to hear a man's voice answering your phone, I caught on to your deception pretty quickly. I simply told her the truth, that we'd gone fishing and you were upstairs changing your clothes."

She hadn't wanted to deceive her parents, but every time she had tried to explain, the words just wouldn't come. What was she supposed to have done, she wondered bitterly, calmly announce her new position in life as Steve's mistress?

The question brought relief in anger. "I was only trying to protect them," she cried.

"You mean you were protecting yourself," he corrected harshly. "Mommy and Daddy's little girl was afraid to tarnish her image by behaving like a grown woman!"

"What would you know about it?" She eyed him with condemnation as she jerked upright, too rattled to consider the cruelty of what she was about to say. "You've never had anyone who gave a damn about you, so don't try and tell me how I should treat two people who love me!"

She heard his swift inhalation of breath and stared at him in horror. "Steve, I didn't mean . . ."

His face had gone a pasty gray. "I don't think I can stomach hearing what you meant."

He turned to leave the room, then hesitated on the landing. "But you're right about one thing," he said quietly. "I've never had anyone who gave a damn about me, Christina."

CHAPTER TEN

Christina was frozen in place, and she couldn't make herself go to Steve. She stared at him and felt an alienation that ripped through the entire fabric of their relationship. His statement went around and around in her brain. "I've never had anyone who gave a damn about me." Those words had been meant for her, and she couldn't blame him for thinking that way.

With her he had lowered his defenses and had begun to believe she cared for him. Now, because of a stupid, selfish evasion of the truth, she had denied him. As surely as everyone else in his life, she had betrayed his trust, But she had to make him understand, she thought frantically, she had to!

"That's not true," she whispered. "I . . ."

He looked across the distance separating them, his face devoid of expression. "You what, Christina?"

"I love you."

There wasn't a trace of amusement in the laugh

he uttered. "Do you?" he asked coldly. "I didn't think love was something to be ashamed of."

"It isn't," she began eagerly, anxious to make him understand.

But the hurt in his eyes had too much sway over him at that moment, and he silenced her with a shake of his head. "You know, you and my grandmother have more in common than I realized, Christina. She was ashamed, too, but at least she was honest enough to admit it."

"You're not being reasonable, Steve." She stiffened her spine and slid to the edge of the chair. "You were the one who put a limit to what we've shared. No promises, remember?"

His shoulders slumped, and he leaned against the banister for support. "You're right, I'm not being reasonable," he agreed tiredly. "I knew you hated the idea of being my mistress."

"It was all you wanted from me."

She saw a muscle pulse in his cheek, and he swallowed heavily before he qualified. "It was all I asked for."

"I can remember your exact words when I wanted to know what you felt for me."

Her voice was laced with a disillusion she didn't try to hide. "You very reluctantly said you cared, but in the same breath you admitted you didn't want all the ties that bind."

"I was thinking of your welfare as well as my own," he explained impatiently. "Eventually you would have quit looking at me through the rose-colored glasses of a romantic."

"Just how was I going to explain that to my parents, Steve? Was I supposed to admit I was just a temporary bedmate, and that you had no intention of ever marrying me?"

He bowed his head, hiding the expression in his eyes. "I never thought—"

"Of course you didn't," she interrupted in a scathing voice. "You've never wanted responsibility or commitment to enter into our relationship, and I've had to accept that. But when you love someone you try to protect their feelings, and you do your best to make them happy. That's what I've tried to do for you, as well as for my mom and dad. If that means I've based our relationship on lies and deception, then I guess I'm guilty as charged."

Steve took one step forward, and then another. "Honey, I'm sorry I overreacted. I had no right to be both judge and jury, and I guess I was too damn mad to view your actions rationally."

But there was still a thread of doubt in his voice, which Tina interpreted accurately. Trying desperately to mask her disappointment, she asked, "Why did my mother phone?"

"She and your father are coming for a short visit in a couple of weeks," he replied hollowly, "and if their timing isn't convenient with your schedule she wants you to call her back."

"It's been a long time since I've seen them."

He moved slowly forward until he stood directly in front of her, and his eyes were somber as he studied her features. "What happens now, Christina?"

A shadow deepened the green of her eyes, and her voice was barely discernible as she asked, "What do you mean?"

"You've gone to a lot of trouble to keep our cohabitation a secret, and I realize now just how difficult it's been for you to compromise your principles to live with me."

"Get to the point, Steve," she insisted impatiently. "What are you trying to say?"

Muttering a terse expletive, he spun away from her and halted in front of the dresser. All Christina could see was his broad back beneath his blue chambray shirt, but she had no trouble distinguishing each word he spoke when he asked, "I suppose you'll be moving out now?"

A wound was inflicted on her heart in that instant, and she began to bleed inwardly. Closing her eyes to contain her anguish, she whispered, "Is that what you want?"

Steve looked at her with pain and confusion in his eyes. He shrugged his shoulders and left the room.

Her eyes filled with tears as she stood alone, her mind a blank and her heart too damaged to grieve.

In the week that followed their confrontation, they avoided the question that had been left unanswered. They functioned as polite strangers, each of them avoiding the other as much as possible.

On the surface little seemed changed between them, but because of Steve's indecisiveness, there was an undercurrent of tension that belied their casual behavior. When they talked at dinner, only impersonal subjects were discussed, both of them careful to avoid any conflict. The most obvious result of their inner turmoil was physical. Steve began working late in his office, waiting until she was asleep, or pretending to be, before seeking his bed. In the morning he was gone, only the rumpled pillow indicative of his presence.

They were behaving in such a civilized manner that Tina was sickened by the whole situation. She couldn't believe the closeness they'd shared over the past months now counted for nothing, and yet with each day that went by Steve was withdrawing farther into himself and away from her. He was distant and preoccupied, almost as though she had already left him in his mind. His attitude fueled her resentment. If he wouldn't say whether he wanted her to stay or to go, then, she told herself, one of them had to make a move, had to take the responsibility for ending what had become an intolerable situation.

She began looking for another apartment to rent, but in her perverse mood nothing suited her requirements. She spent endless hours wandering through impersonal rooms, trying to drum up some enthusiasm. But everything she saw was either too small and cramped, or too large and expensive. When she finally acknowledged her reluctance to leave the house where she'd known such happiness, she railed at herself for her lack of pride.

But she soon faced the fact that pride was cold comfort when measured against the pointlessness of a future without Steve. She didn't want to be proud and alone, and she didn't want to live the rest of her life longing for what might have been. When she realized she was already doing exactly that, she began to get mad. And the angrier she got, the greater the injustice she felt.

Steven Michaels was a mule-headed, blind, stupid cowboy without the sense to appreciate what he was giving up—namely her. If he didn't want to marry her, that was just fine and dandy, she decided, but she was damned if she was going to let herself be discarded like an old boot. If he wanted her to go he was going to have to tell her so, she vowed passionately, and in no uncertain manner!

So she waited for him to bring up the subject, but one day followed another without a word being spoken. She didn't know whether to be elated or morose. One moment she interpreted his silence as an unwillingness to rock the boat, and the next she was certain he just didn't care enough to open his big mouth.

Only gradually did she begin to analyze the inconsistency in his behavior, and she was suddenly convinced that the last thing he wanted was for her to leave. Sometimes, when he didn't know she was watching him, she could have sworn his eyes were clouded with bleak despair. Although she realized her imagination could be working overtime, she tried to lift her flagging confidence by assuring herself he still wanted her. The only problem was, she couldn't figure out how she was going to get him to admit it!

To her chagrin it was her sweet, unworldly mother who came up with the solution. Tina had put off calling until Steve was with a potential buyer, putting two of his prized yearlings through their paces in the training arena. She didn't want to take the chance of his walking in on her. Although confident that she wouldn't burst into tears upon hearing her mother's beloved voice, that was exactly what she did the moment she opened her mouth.

She managed to temper her hysteria enough to explain the mess she'd gotten herself into, and finally ended her story by saying, "Oh, Mom, I've been such an idiot!"

Helen Carlson's reply was immediate. "Yes, dear, I'm afraid you have."

Sullenly, Tina sniffled into the phone. "I'm sorry for disappointing you, but I loved him so much nothing else seemed to matter at the time."

"And I'm sorry you didn't feel you could confide in your father and me," she remarked calmly. "Whether we approved your decision or not, we love you enough to have understood."

"I don't know why I ever thought you wouldn't."

"Because you still see us through the eyes of a child, darling," Helen replied, "wanting our approval of your choices and decisions. It's very flattering to know that our opinion matters so much to you, but it shouldn't outweigh what you think is best for you, or make you afraid to tell us what's going on in your life."

Tina was silent, absorbing all that her mother had said, then asked, "What am I going to do, Mother?"

There was a prolonged silence. "I'm afraid there's only one solution, dear. Men are notoriously awkward when push comes to shove, so you're just going to have to persuade him to your way of thinking."

She cocked her head to stare at the telephone receiver with disbelieving eyes. There were two constructions she could place on the advice she'd been given, but surely her mother hadn't meant that the way it sounded!

Clearing her throat didn't keep it from squeaking, but she questioned her annoyingly vague parent anyway. "Just how am I supposed to do that?"

Tina could have sworn she heard a girlish giggle on the other end of the line, but she couldn't be certain. "I'm sure you'll think of something," Helen replied.

Tina sounded disgusted. "A lot of help you are!"

Obviously Helen agreed, because she quickly

added, "From what you've told me about Steve, he sounds like a fine man. Why don't you try trusting him, Tina?"

Her reply was disgruntled. "But I do!"

"No, you don't," her mother corrected gently. "If you did, you would be confident of his feelings for you."

"You're right," Tina whispered, after she'd taken a moment to digest what she'd been told. "I've been so concerned with proving to him that he could trust me, I didn't bother learning to trust him."

"Love and trust go hand in hand, sweetheart."

Tina nodded, forgetting that her mother couldn't see her. "If Steve hadn't begun to trust me, he wouldn't have been so hurt and angry when he thought I was denying our relationship, would he?"

Helen Carlson knew her daughter's logical mind well. There was a smile in her voice when she said, "No, dear."

"And we were happy together until you called."

Showing no sign of hurt at Tina's blunt realization, Helen replied, "Yes, dear."

"Mother," Tina shouted, her eyes blazing with sudden conviction, "that man loves me!"

There was a gurgle of laughter on the other end of the line. "Yes, dear," Helen agreed complacently. "It really sounds as though he does."

The second she got off the phone, Tina grabbed her coat and purse and headed for the garage. She had enough time to get to town before the shops closed, and there was a gleam in her eye that boded ill for anyone who got in her way. There was a certain boutique she wanted to visit, and when she remembered the type of merchandise they specialized in, her teeth flashed in an expectant grin.

It was where Steve had bought her sexy teddy, the one she'd ripped to pieces in a fit of pique. She regretted her childish behavior now, but she wasn't going to waste time brooding about it. There was only one thought that held any importance in her mind, and as she drove she chanted the words under her breath. "You're going to get yours, Mr. Michaels. Boy, are you going to get yours!"

Steve climbed the veranda steps. He was exhausted, his weariness bone deep and soul-wide. At forty years of age he shouldn't feel like an old man, but he did. Night after night he lay beside Christina, as rigid as a cement slab. The only difference between him and the foundations of this house, he thought, was that they would endure long after he'd fallen to pieces.

It was the nights he hated the most. They were torturous seconds that passed into minutes and hours so slowly he thought he would go mad. He was able to absorb Christina's scent and warmth through his pores, and when she moved or moaned in her sleep it took all of his willpower to keep from grabbing her. His need was beginning to destroy his resolve, and he knew if he continued much longer in this hellish limbo he was going to lose any altruistic motives he'd ever had.

Isn't that what you want? mocked a voice in his head. *Aren't you looking for any excuse to beg her to stay? She's told you she loves you, so why don't you prey on her temporary aberration and tie her to you so tightly she'll never escape?* Steve's mouth twisted at his cruel thoughts, his hand heavy on the doorknob as he stepped into the hallway.

He had always known the day would come when she'd want to leave him, so why couldn't he resign himself to a future without her? *Because it's too soon,* that inner voice taunted. *You didn't think you'd lose her this soon!* But would time really have made any difference? He already knew the answer, and with a vicious swipe of his hand he slammed the door behind him.

"You're late!"

He was irritated with himself for jumping at the sound of Christina's voice, and his reply was harsher than he'd intended. "I'm aware of the time."

She was enticingly close to him, her hands planted on her hips as she asked, "And are you also aware that I've had dinner ready for nearly an hour?"

She sounded so much like a nagging wife, he would have smiled but the thought hurt too much. Instead he glared at her, belligerence in his stance, "If you'd told me I had to be home before dark,"

181

he said, "I would have minded you like a good boy."

"I forgot," she remarked in dulcet tones. "You don't like a woman dogging your footsteps."

When she turned toward the kitchen, he watched the sway of her hips in the loose shift dress she wore, and thought she could dog his steps anytime she wanted. His sarcasm had been unwarranted, but he was too keyed up to offer any conciliatory words as he followed her. "Do I have time for a shower?"

She waved an arm from her position in front of the stove and said, "I can make time, Steve. I've had a difficult day, and I'm sorry I sounded like such a shrew."

Probably tired herself out apartment hunting, he concluded sadly, but all he said was, "I'll only be about fifteen minutes." He glanced at the bare kitchen table. "Aren't we eating in here?"

"I thought we'd use the dining room tonight," she replied absently, vigorously stirring something in a pot.

"Any particular reason?" he asked guardedly.

She turned her head to give him a smile of such sweetness that he almost melted into a puddle right there on the spot. He couldn't help thinking Christina would kill him if he stained her precious hardwood floor, and he could feel his lips trying to twitch into a grin. She didn't know it, but even after she was gone this would be, in his mind, her

182

floor, her kitchen, and her house. Just as he would remain her man.

He had completely forgotten the question he'd asked, and turned to leave. When she answered, he was glad she couldn't see the expression of dread on his face. "We have something to discuss, Steve," she said quietly. "I decided the dining room would be a more comfortable setting for our conversation."

As he nodded abruptly and continued on his way, he no longer felt old . . . he felt ancient.

Christina was peeking around the living room entry, waiting for Steve's return. Her mouth was dry, and her heart was keeping time with her racing pulse. When she heard his footsteps on the stairs she gulped, and raced back to the kitchen. She drew several ragged breaths to calm herself, and then poked her head through the kitchen door. "Go ahead and sit down," she invited with every evidence of cheerfulness. "Everything's already loaded on the serving cart, and I just have to uncork the wine."

Following her suggestion, Steve moved stiffly, but his mouth was tightly compressed as he glowered down at the table. Her antique tablecloth was spread over the surface, and there was a colorful flower arrangement in the center with scented candles burning on either end. There was no other light in the room, which suited his depressed mood. She was certainly celebrating her forthcoming freedom with style, he decided dourly.

"Isn't this cozy?"

He glanced up, and his mouth flew open in shock. Tina was standing behind the serving cart, dressed in one of the most seductive, erotic, and downright lascivious outfits he'd ever clapped his eyes on. Two tiny scraps of midnight-blue gauze covered her breasts and hips, and there was a frilly white, totally transparent bib apron tied around her tiny waist.

"God!" he whispered fervently, just before his knees buckled and he dropped into his chair.

Tina revolved slowly, balancing on three-inch-heeled slippers like a graceful ballerina. "Do you like it?"

Steve thought his eyes were going to bug out of his head, and although he licked his lips he only managed to utter another strangled plea to the Almighty.

Tina bent her head, her loose, wavy hair swinging forward to hide a mischievous grin. Snapping open a white linen napkin, she placed it on his lap and noticed the effect her appearance was having on him. She managed not to crow with triumph, and instead placed her hand against his forehead.

"Are you feeling all right?" she asked. "You look a little flushed."

Her innocent expression was wasted on Steve. His eyes were glued to her breasts, his attention fixed on twin cherry nubs that made his mouth water. "I'm fine," he croaked hoarsely.

"That's good."

She turned quickly and bent over to reach for a bowl, and he sucked in his breath. Now as well as a watering mouth he had itchy hands to contend with, his gaze raptly inspecting two lush mounds bisected by midnight-blue string. He was more than a little flushed, he thought incredulously, he was burning alive!

Tina transferred bowls and plates and cutlery to the table with efficient ease, and then seated herself beside him. He still hadn't spoken a word, and with a little smile she placed her own napkin in her lap. She felt as if she were perched on top of an active volcano, and calmly waited for the eruption to occur.

With a guttural moan Steve jumped up and slammed his fist on the table. "What are you trying to do, Christina?"

She tilted her head and ruined the regal gesture by wrinkling her nose. "Actually, I'm trying to seduce you," she admitted. "Am I having any success?"

"You know damned well you are," he roared, his eyes shooting golden sparks as he jerked her to her feet.

"Aren't you going to untie my apron?"

"You know damned well I am."

She linked her arms around his neck. "Are we going to make love?"

185

This time he smiled, and whispered softly, "You know damned well we are."

Since Tina was alternately kissing his throat and blowing in his ear as he carried her, they never made it as far as the bedroom. With desperate eyes Steve laid his precious burden down on the living room carpet and frantically began to tear at his clothes.

Stretching languidly, she smiled up at him with the confidence of a born seductress. "So you *do* still want me," she murmured.

A button popped off his shirt and flew across the room, but Steve didn't even notice. He was too busy loving her with his eyes. "I'll always want you, honey."

She arched her back and reached behind her to remove the apron. She threw it over her head and smiled. "That sounds like a promise, Steve."

He nodded and knelt at her side. "I'll promise you anything if you'll stay with me."

She sighed and asked tremulously, "Marriage, and children, and forever?"

He shrugged out of his shirt, and it joined her apron on the rug. "If that's what you want."

She stilled his hands as he began to untie the remaining bits of her seduction campaign, her green eyes shadowing with doubt. "Is it what you want, Steve?"

He brushed her hands aside and continued removing the evidence. "It's what I've come to want."

"Why didn't you tell me you were feeling this way?"

He absorbed her hurt into himself and felt whole. "Because I didn't have any confidence in your feelings for me," he admitted. "I told myself that sooner or later you'd want to leave."

"And now?"

Tina waited tensely for his reply, and as he slipped the final scraps of cloth from her body his voice was filled with certainty. "Now I know just how much of yourself you've already given to me. You wanted commitment, and I offered you a temporary place in my life. You wanted marriage, and I made you my mistress. After the way I've treated you, if you haven't left me yet you never will, my love."

Tears filled her eyes, and she placed a trembling hand over his heart. "Your love?"

"My love," he repeated gently.

With a choked cry she catapulted into a sitting position and threw herself into his arms. "I could never leave you, darling."

Steven Michaels looked into Tina's gentle green eyes and saw a promise. He listened to the beat of her heart and heard forever. He remembered the loneliness of his past and thought only of the future.

"I love you so much," he whispered against her mouth.

Spring had arrived, the cold of winter melted away by the flame of love in their hearts. It was a time of harvest, and together they had created the most beautiful garden in the world.